Foreword

CIRIA's research programme *Methane and associated hazards to construction* provides a series of guidance documents for the construction industry.

In addition to a bibliography relevant to methane and construction (CIRIA Special Publication 79) and a study of the construction industry's need for research and information on methane (CIRIA Project Report 5), the other publications of the programme reports on the occurrence and hazards of methane (CIRIA Report 130), on detection, measurement and monitoring (CIRIA Report 131), on protecting development from methane (CIRIA Report 149), on strategies of investigating sites for methane (CIRIA Report 150), and on the assessment of risk (CIRIA Report 152).

This report complements Report 131 on gas measurement methods by providing guidance on the application and interpretation of the measurement results. As such it addresses the link between the choice of investigation strategy and the critical design determinant of the risk assessment.

The report was written by Mr C. R. Harries, Mr P. J. Witherington and Mr J. M. McEntee of Wimpey Environmental Limited under contract to CIRIA.

Following CIRIA's usual practice, the research study was guided by a Steering Group which comprised:

Dr A P Tyrrell (chairman)	–	Frank Graham Consulting Engineers Ltd.
Dr J R F Burdett	–	Fire Research Station, Building Research Establishment
Mr E J Farr	–	Northumbrian Environmental Management Ltd
Mr C Grant	–	Department of the Environment
Mr N Pye	–	Kent County Council
Mr M V Smith	–	LTG Environmental Services
Mr J Steeds	–	W S Atkins Environment
Mr H Williams	–	Wallace Evans

CIRIA's Research Manager for this project was Mr F M Jardine.

ACKNOWLEDGEMENTS

The project was funded under Phase III of the programme *Methane and associated hazards to construction* by :

Department of the Environment, Construction Directorate
Northumbrian Water Ltd   Lothian Regional Council
North West Water Ltd   CIRIA Core Programme.

CIRIA and Wimpey Environmental Ltd are grateful for help given to this project by the funders, by the members of the Steering Group and by the many individuals and organisations who were consulted.

Contents

Figures

Boxes

Tables

Glossary

Aerobic In the presence of free oxygen.

Alkalinity The quantitative capacity of a water to neutralise a strong acid.

Anoxic In the absence of oxygen.

Anaerobic A condition in which oxygen is absent and the environment is also in a chemically reduced state.

Aromatic An organic compound containing a benzene ring structure.

Attenuation The reduction in concentration of chemical species present in liquid seeping from the foot of a landfill as a result of its passage through soil or rock.

Biochemical methane potential (BMP) A measure of the amount of methane that can be produced from a material by the action of micro-organisms.

Biochemical oxygen demand (BOD) A measure of the amount of a material which can be oxidised by micro-organisms.

Biogas A blend of gases principally methane and carbon dioxide produced by the decomposition of organic matter under anaerobic conditions.

Biogenic Produced by the action of micro-organisms.

Chemical oxygen demand (COD) A measure of the total amount of chemically oxidisable material present in a waste.

Emission rate The volume of gas escaping from an area of ground or a structure per unit of time. In this report the term is used to describe the quantity of gas emitted per unit area of ground surface. Sometimes used to refer to velocities of gas leaving a borehole or standpipe.

F_{420} A coenzyme common to all methanogenic bacteria and involved in methane generation.

Free energy change (ΔG^{6}) The energy produced or consumed by a reaction under standard conditions ($25°C$, 1 atmosphere pressure in water at pH 7.0). Negative values are energy yielding reactions, positive values are energy consuming reactions.

Gas flow The volume of gas moving through a permeable medium or down a pipe per unit of time.

Groundwater	Water associated with soil or rock layers below ground level in the saturated zone of the water table.
Isotope	One of two or more forms of an element differing from each other in atomic weight, and in nuclear but not chemical properties.
Methanogenic	Methane producing.
Methane oxidising	Capable of using methane as a carbon source for growth and metabolism by consuming it aerobically.
Oxidation	The addition of oxygen, removal of hydrogen or loss of electrons during a chemical reaction.
pH	A measure of the acidity or alkalinity of a liquid in terms of the hydrogen ion concentration.
Permeability	A measure of the rate of flow of a liquid or gas through a porous medium.
Recalcitrant	Non-biodegradable or degraded so slowly as to be considered non-biodegradable.
Reduction	The removal of oxygen, addition of hydrogen or addition of electrons during a chemical reaction.
Sampling	Collection of a portion of material for experimentation such that the material taken is representative of the whole.
Stoichiometry	The quantitative relationship between reacting substances.
Total organic carbon (TOC)	A measure of the amount of carbon present in the organic fraction of a waste.
Volatile fatty acids (VFA)	Organic acids produced during the acidogenic phase of the anaerobic decomposition of organic matter.
Volatile solids (VS)	Material that can be removed at relatively low temperatures ($<600°C$) and usually referring to the organic fraction.
Xenobiotic	Not naturally produced or present in the environment.
Zone of influence	The volume of ground surrounding a standpipe or other gas investigation installation which can or is being influenced by the use or control of that installation.

Notation

Ar	Argon
$CaCO_3$	Calcium carbonate
CH_4	Methane
CO_2	Carbon dioxide
CO	Carbon monoxide
$\Delta G^{\acute{o}}$	Free energy change
H_2	Hydrogen
H_2S	Hydrogen sulphide
He	Helium
N_2	Nitrogen
O_2	Oxygen

Abbreviations

BMP	Biochemical methane potential
BOD	Biochemical oxygen demand
BSI	British Standards Institution
BRE	Building Research Establishment
CEC	Commission of the European Communities
COD	Chemical oxygen demand
DIAL	Differential absorption LIDAR
DoE	Department of the Environment
EPA	Environmental Protection Act 1990
GC	Gas chromatography
HDPE	High density polyethylene
HMIP	Her Majesty's Inspectorate of Pollution
HSE	Health and Safety Executive
ICE	Institution of Civil Engineers
ICRCL	Interdepartmental Committee on the Redevelopment of Contaminated Land
LIDAR	Light detection and ranging
LDPE	Low density polyethylene
LEL	Lower explosive limit
LFG	Landfill gas
MEWAM	Methods for the examination of waters and associated materials
MS	Mass spectrometry
NCB	National Coal Board
OEL	Occupational exposure limit
ppm	Parts per million
uPVC	Unplasticised polyvinyl chloride
STP	Standard temperature and pressure, 0°C and 1 atmosphere.
TOC	Total organic carbon
TS	Total solids
VFA	Volatile fatty acids
VS	Volatile solids

1   Introduction

The objective of this CIRIA project is to improve the interpretation and understanding of investigation and measurement techniques as applied to ground gases. It should also assist with the correct understanding of ground gas regimes and the risk posed by the generation and movement of gases on affected sites. This should enable better assessments of risk and design of appropriate gas protection measures to be undertaken.

This report represents one of two studies in the final phase of the CIRIA programme: *Methane and associated hazards to construction.* The complete programme consists of eight projects with their resulting reports:

- A bibliography of 500 references relating to the occurrence of methane at construction sites (CIRIA Special Publication 79).

- A guidance document on the nature, origins and occurrence of methane (CIRIA Report 130).

- A guidance document on the methods of detection, sampling, measurement and monitoring of methane (CIRIA Report 131).

- A study to establish the priorities for research and information needed by the construction industry in relation to methane hazards (CIRIA Project Report 5).

- The protection of new and existing developments from methane and associated gases in the ground (CIRIA Report 149).

- Procedures for the investigation of sites for methane and associated gases in the ground (CIRIA Report 150).

- The interpretation of subsurface gas concentrations (this report).

- The assessment of degrees of risk (CIRIA Report 152).

The CIRIA programme therefore addresses the identification and investigation of ground gas regimes as well as the interpretation of measurements of methane and other hazardous gases arising from the ground. It then considers the assessment of risk attributable to the gases present and the methods which can be used to ensure the safety of developments on gas-affected ground.

These subjects were identified as high priority needs of the construction industry.

1.1   SCOPE OF THE REPORT

This report will provide the practitioner of ground gas investigations with a logical process for the development of a reliable conceptual model defining the ground gas regime on a gas contaminated site. The model can then be used for defining risk and potential liability and for the design of any remedial works necessary. This report considers the value and limitations of different investigation and measurement techniques, factors which might influence those measurements and the value of different techniques for developing an understanding of subsurface gas regimes. As CIRIA's methane programme is an integrated series of studies, overlap between individual reports is inevitable. However, extensive cross reference to the other reports is made to assist the reader in utilising the most relevant guidance for his particular requirements.

Since the Loscoe incident in 1986 (Williams and Aitkenhead, 1989) and the subsequent publication of the first edition of Waste Management Paper 27 in 1989 (DOE, 1989a) the measurement of subsurface gas concentrations has become a far more familiar part of ground investigations prior to redevelopment as well as for routine safety assurance purposes. Emphasis is placed on the concentrations of the principal constituent gases of landfill, mine and marsh gases, namely methane and carbon dioxide, although the presence of other gases receives some consideration. The presentation of guidance concentration levels for methane and carbon dioxide in WMP 27 (1st Edition) and their revision in the subsequent 2nd Edition in 1991 (DoE, 1991) has resulted in most investigation work having an emphasis on the measurement of the concentrations of these gases. Such measurements are of limited value in understanding the gas producing activity of the 'ground' or in quantifying the risk to structures and persons on the site. Rather, the risk is a function of the gas composition being produced, the rates of production or flow in the ground, and the presence of gas migration pathways and targets.

Measurement of gas concentration in boreholes, standpipes, spike holes and other such monitoring installations gives only a crude indication of the methanogenic activity of the site. The measured concentrations are frequently no more than a reflection of the gas production, standpipe/well design and use, site surface permeability, weather conditions and other variables.

One aim of this study is to increase the awareness of ground investigation practitioners to the potential of techniques other than simple gas concentration measurement and to promote better use of site measurements and other information to give greater understanding of gas-affected sites.

This report has been compiled with the advice and comment of experts in the field of gas investigation, researchers, practitioners and regulators in related fields and with the technical guidance of the project steering committee, for which the authors are grateful.

1.2   STRUCTURE AND USE OF THE REPORT

This report will assist the practitioner to develop a reliable conceptual model of the ground gas regime at the site being investigated. Such models will then form the basis of the risk assessment and subsequent design of any necessary remediation or protective measures.

The overall CIRIA methane research programme provides a basic understanding of ground gas, deals with information collection and site investigation and concludes with risk assessment and remediation design. The conceptual model draws all the elements of the research programme together. The complete process is represented diagrammatically in Figure 1.1 where reference to the individual reports is given showing the structure of the overall programme.

Because of the central role of the conceptual model, this report necessarily overlaps with the other reports in the research programme. The contents of this report, which are also referenced in Figure 1.1, are structured as follows:

- Needs for gas measurement   Section 2
- Origin and nature of ground gas   Section 3
- Factors influencing ground gas   Section 4
- Ground gas measurement   Section 5

• Ground gas sampling	Section 6
• Strategy for data collection	Section 7
• Interpretation and use of results – development of a conceptual model	Section 8
• Limitations in current practice and recommendations for improvement	Section 9

The report centres around Section 8 where a flow chart for developing the conceptual model is given. The section, however, is fundamentally dependent upon the preceding parts and the other reports in the research programme. To assist the reader, extensive cross reference is made to the relevant previous sections and the remainder of the research programme. The reader may proceed directly to Section 8 and use it as an index to this report. In addition, Figure 1.1 can be use as a key to the complete CIRIA methane research programme.

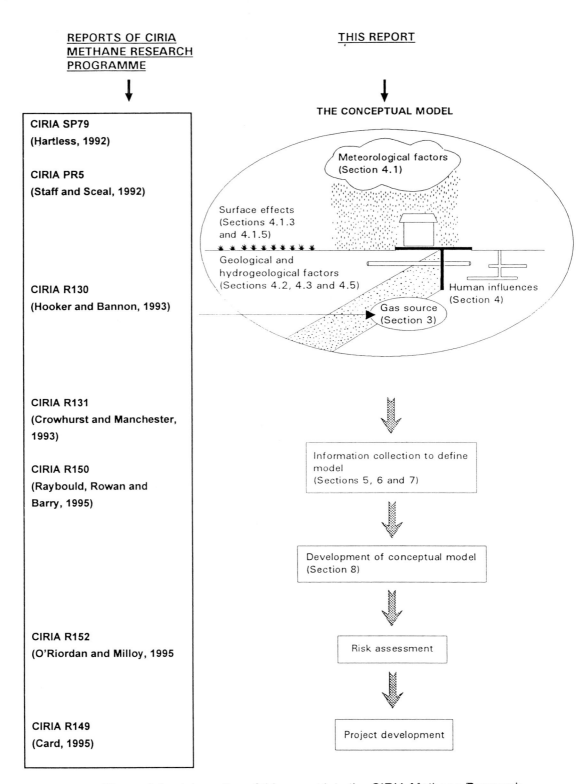

Figure 1.1 Integration of this report into the CIRIA Methane Research Programme

2   The need for gas measurements

The ground gases considered in this report are generally of a potentially harmful nature. The hazards they present include the potential for explosion, asphyxiation, poisoning, retardation of plant growth and increase of the greenhouse effect in the earth's atmosphere. In view of the potential severity of these hazards, there is need for measurement and understanding of ground gas conditions and an ability to assess the consequent risk from ground gases to any particular activity on a site.

Specific reasons for taking and interpreting gas measurements include:

1. The safe design of new development.

2. The assessment of risk to existing development or land usage and the design of appropriate remediation if required.

3. The assessment of risk and liability resulting from gas migration to adjoining sensitive targets.

4. Legal requirements. A statutory duty is placed upon Waste Regulation Authorities and Local Authorities to collect ground gas data in certain circumstances. Furthermore, legal obligations can be placed on landowners and landfill operators by planning and licence conditions to perform ground gas monitoring on a regular basis.

5. Insurance company stipulations.

Situations which may give rise to the need to undertake ground gas investigations are summarised in Table 2.1.

Table 2.1 Reasons for ground gas investigation

Activity	Reason for investigation
New housing, commercial, recreational or other civil engineering developments	Planning permission – building control, environmental health Design precautions Funding Insurance Safety
Existing development or change of ownership	Safety Legal commitments Assessment of need for control measures Design of control measures Due diligence
New landfill	Environmental impact assessment, background levels Site licensing Safety
Existing landfill	Legal obligations of EPA Surrender of licence Safety Gas utilisation
Mining activities	Safety, particularly post-closure

2.1   LEGISLATIVE FRAMEWORK

One of the main factors influencing the need for gas measurements is the potential liability resulting from gas migration away from the source. It is therefore pertinent to outline the current legislative framework (at the time of writing, 1994; readers should also take into account provisions of the Environment Act 1995)..

There are two areas of law which have to be considered:

1. Statute law which can result in criminal liability.
2. Common law which can result in civil liability.

Statute law regarding liability for gas is principally contained in the Environmental Protection Act 1990 (EPA), although the Health and Safety at Work Act, Construction Design and Management Regulations (CONDAM) and Control of Substances Hazardous to Health (COSHH) can also apply.

Sections of the EPA that are particularly relevant to ground gas hazards are:

Section 39 which specifies requirements for the surrender of Waste Management Licences. In particular, licences may not be surrendered until the Waste Regulation Authority (WRA) is satisfied that all potential pollution threats have ceased. The monitoring and analysis criteria for defining the absence of a pollution threat with respect to both leachate and landfill gas are presented in Waste Management Paper 26A (DoE, 1993).

Section 61 places a duty upon Waste Regulation Authorities to carry out inspections of closed waste sites to assess whether they present a potential risk. The authority can recover the cost of any necessary remediation work from the site owner.

Section 79 makes it a criminal offence to cause a statutory nuisance and *Section 80* gives powers to the local authority to serve an abatement notice on any person causing such a nuisance. In this respect the owner of a site may be instructed to prevent the risk of gas migration from that site to a potentially sensitive target.

Box 2.1 Example of enforcement of gas control measures

> The owner of a closed landfill site in West London containing mainly 'inert' waste was instructed by the local authority to install a barrier to prevent gas migration in the direction of an adjacent school. Although monitoring had not indicated migration of landfill gas, the local authority insisted that there was the potential for nuisance. The local authority instruction was not challenged as the site owner agreed to install a barrier at a cost of £60 000.

The important areas of common law which can be applied to the migration of landfill gas are:

Negligence whereby a site owner can be responsible for a negligent act on his part which has caused damage to a neighbour.

The ruling of Rylands v. Fletcher which presents the potential strict and retrospective liability for damage. This means that a site owner can be held responsible for damage resulting from an action he did not knowingly commit. In other words, there is no need for the proof of negligence. This ruling however has recently been challenged in the courts with respect to contamination migration in the case of *Cambridge Water Company v. Eastern Counties Leather Company*. The ruling by the House of Lords, given in December 1993, introduced the test of 'remoteness'. By this means liability only occurs when the damage could have been reasonably foreseen at the time the polluting incident took place. Nevertheless, in EC green paper (CEC, 1993) there has been a proposal to establish community wide strict liability for all pollution damage.

By these statutory and common law provisions, owners can be held responsible for damage resulting from gas migration from their sites. This therefore presents a vital need for reliable measurement and interpretation of ground gas conditions in order to predict the potential for damage.

A useful review of the current relevant legislation and its application to landfill gas related issues is presented in Cooper *et al.* (1993a).

This legislation not only applies to landfill gas but also hazardous gases from other sources. However, liability or responsibility for gases from natural sources such as deep geological strata or peat deposits might be more difficult to assign than for man-made sources such as landfills, coal mines etc.

2.2 AVAILABLE DOCUMENTATION AND GUIDANCE FOR DEVELOPMENT

Several documents published by the Department of the Environment (DoE) give guidance to statutory authorities in England and Wales when assessing gassing or potentially gassing sites.

The benchmark publication is DoE circular 17/89 *Landfill Sites: Development Control* (DoE, 1989b). This circular gives advice to local authorities about the use of their planning powers in relation to landfill gases, and relies upon the guidance provided by Waste Management Papers 4 (HMIP, 1988), 26 (DoE, 1986) and 27 (DoE, 1991), DoE circular 21/87 and the Interdepartmental Committee on the Redevelopment of Contaminated Land (ICRCL) guidance notes 59/83 (ICRCL, 1987) and 17/78 (ICRCL, 1990).

Section 3 of circular 17/89 states that the Secretaries of State consider that if local planning authorities and developers need the guidance given in this circular and in the Waste Management Papers, planning decisions should be taken on a basis which takes account of the risk to development from the migration of landfill gas.

Section 10 states that article 18 of the General Development Order 1988, (DoE, 1988) requires a local planning authority to consult the waste disposal authority concerned before granting planning permission for development within 250 metres of land which is (or has been at any time in the 30 years before the relevant application) used for the deposit of refuse or waste.

Section 19 discusses redevelopment and comments that the redevelopment of land requires planning permission. Where the redevelopment of a closed landfill site or nearby land is involved, even the possibility of difficulties from migrating gas would be a material planning consideration. Where the presence of gas has been discovered, or it is suspected that it may be present during the development of a site, investigations should be carried out to determine the source of the gas and apply any remedial measures to prevent it causing a hazard either during the course of the development or during subsequent use of a site.

The requirements for Building Control are contained in the Building Regulations Approved Document C (DoE, 1992). This document incorporates the main points of guidance on the measures to be incorporated into developments to resist moisture. In addition, general guidance is given to the problems associated with the presence of contaminants including landfill gas and methane. This guidance is based largely on publications of the Building Research Establishment (BRE, 1991) and WMP 27 (DoE, 1991) and states that where there is a potential for gas risk to a building, further investigation should be made to determine what, if any, protective measures are necessary. Where the level of methane in the ground is unlikely to exceed 1% by volume, no further protection needs to be provided if the ground floor of the building is of suspended concrete construction and ventilated.

Approved Document C also states that carbon dioxide should be considered independently of methane. Concentrations of carbon dioxide exceeding 1.5% by volume in the ground indicate a need to consider gas exclusion measures, but where there are concentrations of 5% or more, specific design measures are required.

Despite this guidance, it should not be forgotten that the asphyxiant effects of methane and carbon dioxide are additive. However, concerns over the respective concentrations of these gases should arise at levels below those at which oxygen depletion becomes a serious consideration.

The guidance in the documents referred to above deals mainly with concentrations of methane and carbon dioxide. It considers modern landfill sites which are or have been used at any time in the past thirty years for the deposition of refuse or waste. This time scale is significant in relation to the passing of the Clean Air Act 1956, and the subsequent decline in domestic coal burning as a source of heating. The change to gas- and oil-fired central heating over this period resulted in a substantial increase in the organic content of domestic refuse and its potential to produce landfill gases.

There is little if any specific guidance for sites with other sources of methane or carbon dioxide, such as landfills older than thirty years, landfills containing 'inert' type wastes only, deposits of peat, marshes, coal measures or sites where carbon dioxide is emanating from carbonate minerals or buried vegetation.

Furthermore, there is little available guidance specifically covering the investigation of potentially gassing sites.

BS 5930: 1981 (BSI, 1981) and the *Specification for Ground Investigation* (ICE, 1989), provide detailed guidance for geotechnical investigations, but contain very little information for the investigation of ground gases. DD 175, the draft for development, *Code of practice for the identification of potentially contaminated land and its investigation.* (BSI, 1988) provides detailed guidelines for the investigation of a contaminated site but there is no specific guidance on the investigation of potentially gassing sites.

Other sources of guidance relevant to gas from mines are available (NCB, 1979) and the petrochemical industry also has guidance relating to the escape of gases into the ground from underground storage tanks (Institute of Petroleum, 1993).

Guidance in this whole area is, however, changing and being added to very rapidly. Most recently published are WMP 4 and WMP 26A which form the basis for Waste Management Licensing under the Environmental Protection Act. WMP 4 includes the requirements for monitoring of all emissions into the environment from licensable waste management facilities including landfill sites. WMP26A specifies the required level of monitoring of landfill sites in order for a 'certificate of completion' to be issued. This is necessary for the surrender of a waste management licence, relating to a landfill site, under section 39 of the EPA. This is the first guidance document to discuss the need of measuring gas flow rates and to specify guidance levels based on gas flow rates.

Detailed comments on the available official documentation are provided by Raybould *et al.* (1995).

2.3 REQUIREMENTS OF MEASUREMENTS

There are needs for ground gas measurements which can be used for the assessment of risk and the design of appropriate remediation or control measures. In certain situations information is also required for the design of landfill gas utilisation schemes.

Current official guidance is mainly related to measurements of gas concentrations, but there is usually insufficient knowledge of a ground gas regime for risk to be determined and appropriate control measures designed. These matters can only be properly addressed when the following questions have been answered.

1. What gases are present in the ground?
2. Where are the specific gases of interest?
3. Are the volumes of gas being produced and the ground conditions likely to cause lateral gas movement and, if so, how much and where is it moving or could it move to?
4. How is the gas emitted from the ground?

Deficiencies in understanding of this nature can only be satisfied by more extensive measurement and analysis of site conditions. The range of parameters which might need to be measured in particular situations include:

- the composition of ground gas
- the volumes of gas available in the ground to create a hazard
- rates of gas generation, where the gas is a result of biodegradation
- gas flow rates
- gas pressures
- gas permeabilities of the ground and potential migration pathways
- climatic, geological, hydrogeological and man-made factors which can influence gas generation and movement.

Box 2.2 Critical issues from Section 2

1. Why does ground gas need to be investigated?
2. Is there a need to measure gas quantities as well as concentrations of gas?
3. Is there a need to establish geological structure in order to understand the potential for gas migration?

3   Origins and nature of ground gases

3.1   SOURCES OF GAS IN THE GROUND

Gases present in the interstitial spaces in the ground can be derived from any of the three potential sources discussed below. In most cases, gases beneath the ground surface are a combination of constituent gases from more than one of these sources. The relative contribution from different sources will vary between sites and with time.

3.1.1   Atmospheric gases

Gases contained in the earth's atmosphere enter the ground through surface cracks, pores and fissures and mix with other soil gases in the interstitial spaces of the ground. Atmospheric gases can penetrate the ground as a result of atmospheric pressure fluctuations, diffusion, movement of groundwater levels, or as dissolved gases in rainfall or moving groundwater. It is probable that gas concentrations in the ground are affected by all of the above to some extent. However, the extent of influence by atmospheric gases depends on the gas generation rate in the ground itself, the permeability of the ground and its surface to gas and the magnitude of the driving forces listed above.

The influence of groundwater levels on the penetration of atmospheric gases into the ground can be substantial where the groundwater is subject to tidal variations.

The earth's atmosphere consists principally of nitrogen and oxygen but it also contains other gases, some of which (such as argon and water vapour) are overlooked when evaluating the composition of gas samples. The average gas composition of the earth's atmosphere is shown in Table 3.1.

Table 3.1 Average composition of dry atmospheric air

Gas	Concentration (% by volume)
Nitrogen	78.01
Oxygen	20.95
Argon	0.93
Carbon dioxide	0.03

Gas	Concentration (ppm by volume)
Neon	18.2
Helium	5.2
Krypton	1.1
Xenon	<0.1
Hydrogen	0.5
Methane	2.0
Nitrous oxide	0.5

Notes: All values at standard temperature and pressure (STP)

In practice, air and soil gas samples will contain water vapour which can represent several percent by volume, depending on the temperature and relative humidity

Adapted from WMP 26A (DoE, 1993)

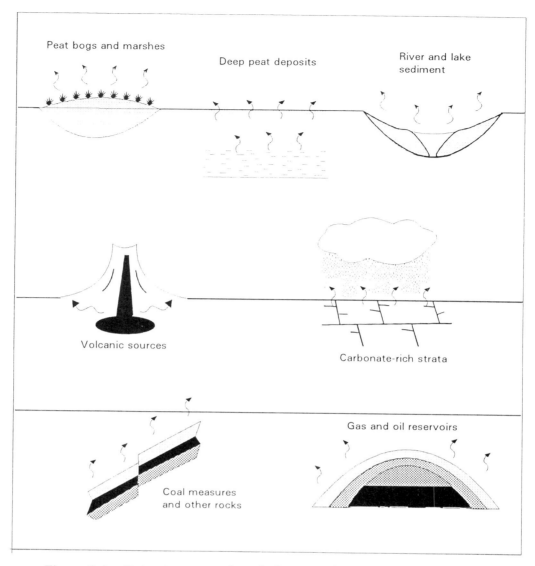

Peat bogs and marshes

Deep peat deposits

River and lake sediment

Volcanic sources

Carbonate-rich strata

Gas and oil reservoirs

Coal measures and other rocks

Figure 3.1 Natural sources of gas in the ground

The extent to which atmospheric gases penetrate the ground depends on the nature of the ground as well as climatic factors. In particular, the permeability of the ground and the volume of interstitial spaces into which the gases can move. Saturation of the ground by water greatly reduces the influence of atmospheric gases on the ground conditions and this is a major factor promoting the establishment of anoxic conditions.

3.1.2 Gases from natural strata

Gases in the ground as a result of their release from natural strata may be derived from deep peat, coal measures, crude oil/natural gas reservoirs, volcanic activity, peat bogs, river and lake sediments or many soils (but particularly organically enriched soils) as illustrated in Figure 3.1. Release of gases from such sources is often promoted by man's activities such as mining which result in a release of pressure on the rock and fragmentation giving rise to the liberation of adsorbed gases or gases contained in vesicles in the rock structure.

In addition, the near-surface geology may release gases from chemical reactions with rainwater, i.e. when the dilute carbonic, sulphuric and nitric acids present in the water react with rocks to liberate carbon dioxide and perhaps other gases in trace concentrations.

Gases derived from natural strata can include methane, carbon dioxide, higher alkanes, hydrogen sulphide, helium, hydrogen, carbon monoxide, and nitrogen.

3.1.3 Man-made sources of gas

Man-made sources of gas in the ground include deposited materials such as landfilled wastes, made ground, infilled docks etc. as well as leakages from pipelines or storage tanks. Some construction materials may also react with the ground to produce gases.

Figure 3.2 shows some of the sources of gas generation resulting from mans' activities.

Gases derived from these sources include methane, carbon dioxide, hydrogen, hydrogen sulphide and nitrogen. In addition, traces of other hydrocarbons such as higher alkanes, aromatics, chlorinated hydrocarbons and numerous other organic gases may be derived from wastes in landfills which have received domestic, commercial or industrial wastes. The trace constituents of landfill gas are listed in WMP 26 (DoE, 1986). Those trace gases not found in 'natural' sources often permit discrimination between natural and man-made sources.

Apart from the direct release of gases from surface deposits, leachates produced by the percolation of rainfall, groundwater, surface water and liquid wastes through a deposit of solid wastes can produce gas at a point in the ground remote from the solid waste deposit.

Gases can be present in the ground as a result of the direct introduction of pure gases or gas mixtures by man, usually because of the unintentional release or leakage of gases from pipelines or tanks buried in the ground.

Leakage of gas from pipelines is most likely to be through leakage from the mains gas delivery pipework which is now used exclusively for supply of natural gas in the UK. However, coal gas or other fuel gases may be encountered in a similar manner where these are conveyed via pipelines. This is likely to involve only short lengths of delivery pipe on industrial sites or between closely situated supplier and consumer as is sometimes the case where commercial utilisation of landfill or mines gas is carried out. The loss of gas from the distribution system has been the subject of a recent British Gas Study (Watt Committee on Energy, 1993) prompted in part by a requirement to quantify methane emissions to atmosphere for reasons of its possible effect on global warming.

Another possibility for point source introduction of gases into the ground includes gas escapes from old sewers, septic tanks, cess pits and soakaways. The escape of the sewage itself and subsequent gas generation in the ground is also a possibility.

Box 3.1   Example of gas derived from a cess pit

A public house with outside toilets backed on to a landfill site. On one occasion a patron using the toilet lit a cigarette. This triggered a small explosion which blew off the door and expelled the patron outside. The following investigation focused on the landfill site as the source of the explosive gas. However, detailed study showed that the toilet drained to a cess pit which was subsequently proved to be the source of methane.

Escapes from subsurface hydrocarbon storage tanks of either vapours or the liquids themselves may also give rise to hydrocarbon gases in the ground.

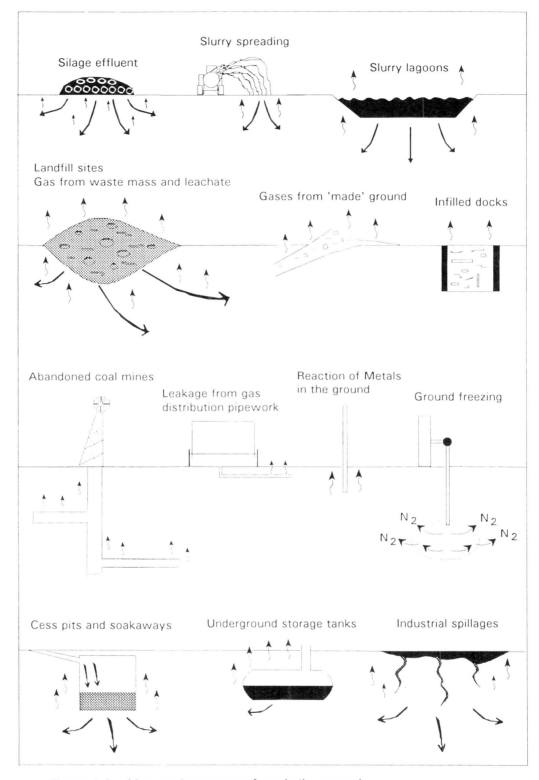

Figure 3.2 Man-made sources of gas in the ground

Many agricultural or industrial fluids such as oils, liquid organic wastes, farm slurries or silage effluent can lead to the production of carbon dioxide in the ground and in some cases significant methane generation in soils upon which such liquids have been spilt or deliberately spread. This is a result of microbial decomposition of the organic compounds in the waste through aerobic or anaerobic processes. An example is given by Elliott and McCalla (1972) who observed methane concentrations to 51.5% and carbon dioxide to 35.5% by volume in soil at a depth of 1.5 m beneath a cattle feedlot in

Nebraska. The gas production was attributed to the organic input in the form of beef cattle manure at the site surface. Methane was found at all levels between 0.3 and 1.5 m below the ground surface. No measurements were made at greater or lesser depths. Interestingly, carbon dioxide concentrations reached 5.0% and averaged 1 to 2.5% by volume, depending on depth, in the soil beneath the cornfield area used as the 'control'.

The reaction of metals with the ground, particularly in acidic soil conditions, can lead to the formation of hydrogen gas. Although the rates of production of hydrogen by such reactions are likely to be low, potentially dangerous incidents have arisen particularly with part-buried metal structures (see Box 3.2). Similar reactions may occur where metal-rich wastes such as certain slags have been deposited.

Box 3.2   Example of hydrogen production by metals in the ground

A welder engaged in the dismantling of a child's tubular steel swing was cutting the swing frame using an oxy-acetylene welder when a sudden ignition of gases, emanating from the frame, occurred. Work was halted and an investigation commenced into the cause of the explosion. Gas samples taken from within the void of the tubular steel frame revealed a flammable concentration of hydrogen even some hours after the initial incident in which the frame had been perforated and the gases ignited. It was concluded that the corrosion reactions of the ground with the steel where it was buried in the ground had resulted in the formation of hydrogen which had then accumulated in the swing frame.

3.2   GROUND GAS COMPOSITION

Most gas samples obtained from the ground consist of blends of gas from more than one ground source or mixtures with atmospheric gases, so a considerable range of gas compositions can be observed from each particular gas source. In addition, the actual composition of gas emitted from different samples from the same type of gas source can vary considerably, particularly from the geological sources. Despite the frequent quoting of ranges of constituent gas concentrations in ground gas samples from different sources, there is, in reality, no lower limit to the concentrations for each constituent gas other than its concentration in atmospheric air. There can be substantial dilution and transformation of migrating gases between source and the point of sampling. It is therefore easier to distinguish the different ground gas sources on the basis of the gas composition, by the presence or absence of certain constituent gases or the ratios between them rather than the actual concentrations.

Typical concentrations for landfill gas are quoted in WMP 26 and 27 (DoE, 1986 and 1991), and gas concentrations for gases from some other sources are presented in Hooker and Bannon (1993). Young (1989) gives some examples demonstrating the different ratios of constituent gases in ground gas samples derived from different sources.

Gases produced by biological decomposition processes under anaerobic conditions in the ground consist predominantly of methane and carbon dioxide, but the ratio of these two gases depends on the substrate undergoing decomposition. The gas composition can be calculated from the stoichiometry of the decomposition as predicted by equations such as those of Buswell and Hatfield (1939), (see Section 5.6.2). For example, carbohydrates such as cellulose or starch would be expected to produce methane and carbon dioxide in a 50:50 ratio, proteins in a 62:38 ratio and lipids (fats) in a 72:28 ratio. The predominance of cellulosic material in most decomposing organic substrates occurring in the ground means that the ratio of these two principal component gases at production is usually close to 50:50. However, the different solubilities of the gases and other reactions can quickly modify this ratio, depending on ground conditions.

Ground gases are also subject to chemical and biological transformations during passage through soils (see Section 4.5). Therefore the ability to discriminate between gases from different sources on the basis of the presence of specific constituent gases is limited, except where certain compounds are present in some ground gases and not in others. An example is the use of trace organic gases as indicators of gas source. Even then, the absence of such gases cannot confirm that the gas sample is not from a source expected to contain them.

Due to the range of concentrations found, the ratios between certain constituent gases have been used as an alternative means of distinguishing gases from different sources. The hydrocarbon ratios, particularly methane to ethane are sometimes used in this fashion, but this approach is only suitable for distinguishing certain gas sources.

Another characteristic of ground gases which has been used to distinguish gas from different sources is the ratio between the different carbon and hydrogen isotopes present as methane and carbon dioxide in gas samples. The $^{14}C:^{12}C$, $^{13}C:^{12}C$ and $^{2}H:^{1}H$ ratios may all be useful. This technique involving mass spectrometric analysis of gas samples studies different isotope ratios to distinguish different gas sources. The radioactive isotope ratios $^{14}C:^{12}C$ are used for carbon dating purposes to distinguish geological sources from recent biogenic sources of methane. However, it is the stable isotope ratios, which differ because of the different conditions of gas formation, that are more useful in distinguishing gas from different sources in the ground.

The use of stable isotope analysis to distinguish gas from different ground sources has been reviewed in Hitchman *et al.* (1990). The technique is better at discriminating between gases from some types of source than others and further data are really needed to clarify the differences, but the technique is the only available method for distinguishing gases from some sources.

However, just as there are changes in gas composition which occur in the ground after the gas has left its source, so there are some changes in the isotope ratios which come about as a result of isotopic separation caused by biological oxidation of the gases or fractionation in passage through a reactive soil.

Figure 3.3 summarises methods available for distinguishing between various pairs of candidate ground gas sources. Not all methods are appropriate for distinguishing each pair of gases but the figure aims to direct the investigator to the most relevant techniques. It is intended as guidance to the investigator who has identified hazardous ground gases on a site, but local information suggests that more than one potential gas source is present in the vicinity.

3.3   RATES OF PRODUCTION OF GROUND GASES

The rates of production or release of gases into the ground or from the ground have been quantified in some cases using field or laboratory methods some of which are detailed in Crowhurst and Manchester (1993). In other cases, rates can be estimated from the principles of the gas-forming reactions responsible. Rates of gas generation are usually quoted either as volumes of gas per unit volume or mass of gassing ground or per unit area of ground surface. If the depth of gassing material is known and the gas is believed to be emitted through the ground surface, the volumetric and areal terms are interconvertible.

	Marsh/peat bogs	Deep peat	Landfill	Made ground	Mines gas	Mains natural gas	Mains coal gas	UG oil/gas reserves
Deep peat	14C							
Landfill	Trace gas	Trace gas 14C						
Made ground	Trace gas	Trace gas 14C	Trace gas					
Mines gas	GC Geology 14C 13C	GC 13C Geology	GC Trace gas Geology 13C 14C	GC 13C 14C Trace gas Geology				
Mains natural gas	GC Pipelines 14C 13C Higher HCs OS	GC Pipelines 13C Higher HCs OS	GC Pipelines Trace gas 13C 14C Higher HCs OS	GC Pipelines 13C 14C Higher HCs OS Trace gas	GC Pipelines 13C OS Geology			
Mains coal gas	GC Pipelines 14C	GC Pipelines 13C	GC Pipelines 14C 13C Trace gas	GC Pipelines 14C 13C Trace gas	GC Pipelines Geology	GC Pipelines 13C		
UG oil/gas reserves	Higher HCs 14C 13C Geology	Higher HCs 13C Geology	Trace gas 13C 14C Higher HCs Geology	Trace gas Higher HCs 14C 13C Geology	GC 13C Geology	GC Pipelines Geology	GC Pipelines Geology	
UG fires	GC	GC	GC	GC	GC Geology	GC Pipelines	Pipelines	GC Geology

Figure 3.3 The application of investigation methods to gas source identification.

Key:

UG	Underground
GC	Gas chromatographic analysis of principal gases, H_2, N_2, O_2, CH_4, CO, CO_2, He, C_2H_6 to determine concentrations and ratios between component gases.
Trace gas	GC or GC-MS analysis of trace organic compounds such as chlorinated HCs, organosulphur compounds, aromatic compounds etc.
14C	Determination of $^{14}C{:}^{12}C$ ratio by mass spectrometry
13C	Determination of $^{13}C{:}^{12}C$ and $^{2}H{:}^{1}H$ ratios by mass spectrometry
Higher Hcs	GC analysis of longer chain alkanes, such as propane (C3) to decane (C10)
Pipelines	Consult relevant bodies or documentation relating to gas/oil distribution pipeline routes.
Geology	Consult sources of geological and mining information.
OS	GC analysis of organosulphur compounds such as mercaptans added to mains natural gas.
Note.	Not all listed techniques will necessarily descriminate gas sources in all cases. For instance, the trace gas content in gas from made ground will depend greatly on the nature of the fill present in the made ground.
	The shaded example indicates that to distinguish mines gas from mains natural gas, the suggested techniques are GC, ^{13}C, OS, the presence of pipelines and geological evidence of coal deposits or mining in the area

3.3.1   Gases from natural sources

Microseeps from underground oil and gas deposits

Crude oil and natural gas deposits in subsurface strata sometimes leak hydrocarbons through permeable rock to the ground surface. Searching for these leakages of hydrocarbon gases is a means of detecting these deposits or of increasing confidence before drilling to assess a potential oil/gas deposit.

Highly tuned gas chromatographs equipped with flame ionisation detectors are used to measure the often low concentrations of hydrocarbon gases in the soil. Quantification of the hydrocarbon-oxidising microbes or their activity in soils has also provided evidence of hydrocarbon flux from subsurface oil reservoirs.

Reports of measured rates of gas production (i.e. release from the underground reservoir) from these sources are limited, but indicate a patchy distribution of emissions dependent on the availability of pathways through the strata overlying the oil reservoir. In the North Sea, one major seepage from petroliferous sedimentary rocks beneath the seabed was found to have a gas flux 1.7×10^7 g CH_4/year. Averaged over the presumed area of influence this was equal to a flux of 26 g CH_4/m^2.year (Hovland and Judd, 1992). This equates to 0.0364 m^3 CH_4/m^2.year at STP. This average rate is relatively low compared to rates from other ground sources but the gas escape is frequently concentrated in microseeps with a considerably higher emission rate than the average over the influenced area.

C1 to C4 hydrocarbons (methane to butane) from petroliferous rock sources have also been observed on land, in soils at concentrations detectable by a simple ground gas survey prior to land redevelopment so the flux of gas can be large enough to produce significant gas concentrations even near the ground surface.

Acid action on carbonate and other minerals

Acids such as sulphuric, nitric and carbonic acids present in rainwater, sulphuric acid from oxidation of sulphide-containing minerals or humic acids from decomposition processes in soils, act on carbonate minerals such as limestone to produce carbon dioxide. Concentrations arising in soils from such processes have been recorded at levels constituting a significant hazard; one case resulted in the asphyxiation of a child entering an open soakaway pit. Many concentration values have been reported, often in the 1–10% range, but no references give the rates of production.

The possible rates of carbon dioxide release from situations dependent on sulphide oxidation and carbonate reaction as the rate depends on a combination of too many physical, chemical and biological factors to make a simple calculation of any value. However, an estimate of the release of carbon dioxide from an area of carbonate rich stratum such as limestone or chalk subject to attack by acid rain impinging on it can be made (Box 3.3).

Figure 3.4 shows a map of atmospheric acid deposition in the UK derived from rainfall monitoring and analysis work carried out by Warren Spring Laboratory. In conjunction with the geological maps of the UK presented in Figure 3.5, it might be expected that the worst areas of the country for carbon dioxide production in the soil as a result of acid reaction with carbonate minerals would be in the counties of Lincolnshire, Nottinghamshire, Humberside and North Yorkshire.

Box 3.3 Production of carbon dioxide by acid reaction with carbonate minerals

Using data contained in the maps presented in Figures 3.4 and 3.5, a site can be envisaged which receives an annual acid deposition of 0.05 g H^+/m^2. If this site also contains abundant carbonate minerals such as chalk or limestone, the production of carbon dioxide may result from rainfall. Protons (H^+) will be present in the rainwater as a result of the solution of carbon dioxide and oxides of nitrogen and sulphur, present in the atmosphere. These protons will then react with chalk or limestone ($CaCO_3$) in the ground to produce bicarbonate in solution or to liberate carbon dioxide gas, depending on the prevailing pH. The formation of bicarbonate is defined by the equation:

$$CaCO_3 + H^+ \leftrightarrow Ca^{2+} + HCO_3^-$$

Bicarbonate exists in solution in water in pH dependent equilibrium with carbonate and dissolved carbon dioxide gas. If further addition of protons occurs, the concentration of bicarbonate will increase. If the pH is depressed further, carbon dioxide will be liberated from solution as gas according to the equilibria:

$$HCO_3^- + H^+ \leftrightarrow H_2CO_3$$

$$H_2CO_3 \leftrightarrow CO_2 \uparrow + H_2O$$

The rate and extent to which carbon dioxide gas evolves as a result of these reactions is highly dependent on the groundwater pH. Assuming all the protons in the rainwater impinging on a site result in CO_2 liberation according to the stoichiometry of the above reactions, then 1 mole of carbon dioxide will be evolved for every 2 protons entering the site in the rain water, i.e. for each g of H^+ (1 mole), 0.5 moles of CO_2 will be produced. One mole of CO_2 will occupy 22.264 litres at STP (a slight deviation from the 24.414 litres occupied by an 'ideal' gas at STP) so this equates to a CO_2 production of 11.13 litres at STP per g of H^+ deposited as atmospheric acid deposition. Therefore it can be calculated that an annual acid deposition of 0.05 g H^+/m^2 would give rise to a carbon dioxide production of 0.5566 litres CO_2/m^2.yr. or approximately 0.0005 m^3/m^2.yr. if complete reaction of deposited acidity with carbonates in the ground occurred. This simple calculation makes certain assumptions. It assumes that total reaction of rainfall acidity with carbonate minerals occurs and it ignores dry deposited acidity. The amount of dry deposited acidity very much depends not only on the presence of acid particulates in the atmosphere but also on the surface vegetation which is important to the entrapment and deposition of particulates in the air. In addition, it assumes that all the CO_2 is liberated as carbon dioxide gas . In reality a lot of it would be removed from the site as dissolved bicarbonate in the ground water. It should also be appreciated that the calculation is based on the annual wet deposition of acid and that great fluctuations in precipitation and its acidity and hence carbon dioxide production by these processes may occur.

However, the indication of the calculations above is that the rates of gas production resulting from the impingement of acidic precipitation on carbonate geology are likely to be low compared with gas production from other sources in the ground such as waste deposits or even the natural respiration processes of microbes in the surface soil.

Using the rainfall data collated by the Warren Spring studies, the potential carbon dioxide release resulting from the impingement of rainwater on carbonate rocks can be estimated for particular regions of the UK in line with the example in Box 3.3.

It is noteworthy that acid rain scientists work with acid deposition rates, i.e. quantities of acid deposited per unit area rather than simple pH i.e. the level of acidity. They have appreciated the value of rate terms rather than concentrations and it is logical that ground gas scientists and engineers should follow suit and move away from the simple reporting of gas concentrations to rate-based units.

There is also a possibility of hydrogen sulphide release from sulphide-containing minerals as a result of acid action on ground, but when such minerals are in the presence of oxygen, biological or chemical oxidation of gaseous (as well as solid) sulphides to sulphates will tend to remove any hydrogen sulphide.

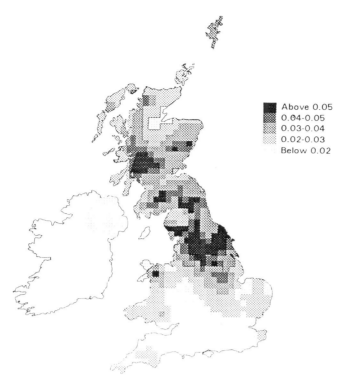

Figure 3.4 Map of wet deposited acid deposition in the U.K. for 1988 (Units in gH^+m^{-2}) (after Warren Spring Laboratory, 1990)

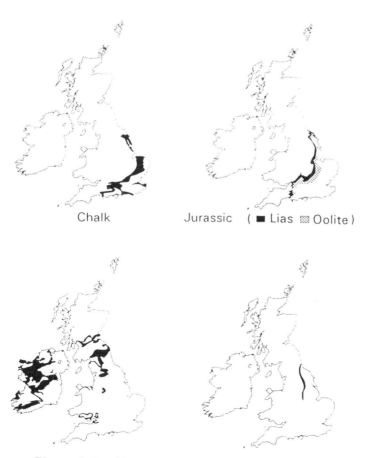

Chalk   Jurassic (■ Lias ▦ Oolite)

Figure 3.5 Simple geological map of the UK showing areas of carbonate geology (after Lousley, 1976)

Coal, volcanic, hydrothermal and other geological sources

It is difficult to assign rates of gas production from the above sources. Volcanic and hydrothermal releases of gas can be intermittent and associated with volcanic activity, earthquakes etc. Coal mine gas emissions are far more significant in this country and can result in hazardous concentrations of methane-rich gases. The release of these gases from the coal is largely dependent on geological or mining disturbance of the coal seams resulting in fragmentation of the coal and release of adsorbed or occluded gases. Hazardous concentrations of carbon dioxide may sometimes form in mines as a result of oxidation processes.

The ventilation system in a working mine is arranged so that any gases entering the mine airways are echausted to the atmosphere through the main surface fan. While the mine is operational there is no opportunity for the uncontrolled escape of gas. The gas content of a coal seam potentially available for emission may be up to 30 m^3/t (Staff *et al.*, 1991).

Gas flows as high as 3200 l/s have been recorded in stimulated recovery wells drilling into virgin coal seams (Creedy, 1991). The emission of gases from disused coal workings is the subject of a recent DoE sponsored study (DoE, 1993).

Closed mines do not necessarily constitute a lesser hazard providing the release of gas is properly controlled. After cessation of mine working the release of gas from the coal is greatly reduced (although it will still constitute a potential hazard). The old mine workings contain a reservoir of gas and subsequent escape of gas from these underground voids is then dependent on changes in atmospheric pressure or water ingress into the mine rather than a flow induced by release of further gas from coal. The emission of gas from the coal typically diminishes to 10% of its initial emission rate within six months of cessation of mining. However, this depends on the partial pressure of gases in the mine atmosphere which determines the rate of gas release, so the maintenance of ventilation is significant in promoting the swift decrease of gas emission from the coal.

Gas release from non-recent deep peat deposits is frequently observed via boreholes penetrating such strata but this is probably due to release of a reservoir of entrapped and adsorbed gas, as with coal, rather than a continuing biological production of gas from the peat organic matter. However, ingress of air to such peat would result in its decomposition to carbon dioxide. This occurs with peat under aerobic conditions resulting from drainage or mixing of peat into surface soils.

Peat bogs and marshes

Gas production from peat in recent bogs and marshes forming the surface layers of ground have been quantified and reported by several authorities. Values quoted in the literature (Svensson 1976) are in the range 0.13 to 30.5 g $CH_4.m^{-2}.yr^{-1}$ and 186 to 1895 g $CO_2.m^{-2}.yr$-1 which is equivalent to 0.18 to 43 litres $CH_4.m^{-2}.yr^{-1}$ and 95 to 965 litres $CO_2.m^{-2}.yr^{-1}$ at standard temperature and pressure.

3.3.2   Man-made sources of gas

Landfills and made ground

Gas production from natural or man-made deposits on the surface of the ground such as bogs, marshes, landfills, etc. are perhaps the best studied in terms of gas generation rates because of their relative accessibility. Gas production rates from landfills or made ground determined by laboratory methods or pumping tests in the field may be as high as 80 m³ CH₄/tonne wet weight/year in very actively decomposing refuse (10 m³ CH₄/tonne/year is more typical) such as on some landfills in which commercial utilisation of gas is undertaken. Highly decomposed waste, so called 'inert' fill, or made ground of very low organic content can produce less than 0.1 m³ CH₄/tonne wet weight/year. Similar rates of carbon dioxide production would be present. Only in the initial stages of waste decomposition when hydrogen and carbon dioxide are the gaseous products of decomposition or towards the end of the decomposition when waste begins to become aerobic again will the composition of the gas being produced, change greatly from the 50:50 mixture of methane and carbon dioxide. Environmental factors such as gas solubility, however, may alter the composition of gas emerging from the ground.

The rates of gas production are highly variable and depend on several factors influencing the rates of the biological activity. These will include the waste temperature, degradable organic content and particle size, the water content and chemical composition of the waste and the stage of degradation of the waste. Highest rates of gas production generally occur when abundant but not inhibitory concentrations of volatile fatty acids, particularly acetic acid are present. In such circumstances which occur in late phase (III) or early phase (IV) of the landfill decomposition as defined by Farquhar and Rovers (1973), (see Figure 3.6), methanogenesis is not limited by availability of substrates. In later stages, decomposition of organic matter, principally cellulose, limits the rate of methane production and rates, though still high, are likely to be lower than before.

Rates of hydrogen production may also be high during phase (II), although, field data for this period are scarce. Laboratory studies, in which, unlike a landfill, all the waste may be of one age, have shown hydrogen production of the order of 23 m³/tonne wet weight/yr for short periods of time (Harries, 1989).

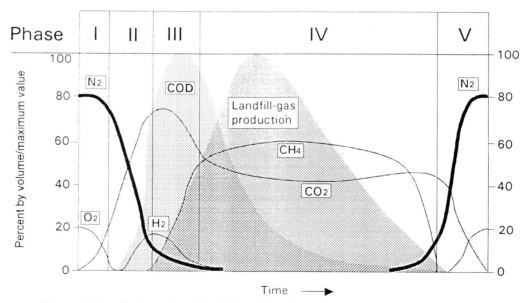

Figure 3.6 Schematic of landfill stabilisation. (adapted from Farquhar and Rovers, 1973 and Pohland, 1986 for WMP 26A, (DoE, 1993)).

Gas leakage from pipelines

The loss of gas as fugitive emissions from pipelines is dependent on the pressures within the pipes, the permeability of the pipe material and the degree of leakage from joints and connections.

Pipe permeability will vary from zero in old cast iron or similar pipework to a very small rate through plastic materials such as HDPE commonly used today for the conveyance of gas and this may be discounted for the purposes of this study. Of greater significance is the loss of gas through small leaks from connections in the system, areas of damage or corrosion.

The total loss from the national gas grid has been the subject of a recent investigation by British Gas detailed in The Watt Committee on Energy (1993) which has attempted to quantify the losses from the complete system by measuring the losses from stretches of pipeline of various ages and materials representative of the network. This study used the loss of pressure in isolated lengths of pipework as the measure of the rate of gas loss. There is considerable variation in leakage from the different parts of the distribution system because of the differences in construction materials, pipe jointing techniques and operating pressures.

This study has been used to calculate a loss of 1.02 % from the British Gas system. As an example the leakage rate from the medium pressure (M.P.) lengths of the distribution network showed a median leakage rate of 0.0367 standard m^3 natural gas/hr/km at 1 bar pressure. The M.P. distribution system operates at 75 mbar to 2 bar pressure. If it is assumed that this gas leakage emanates from a 0.5 m wide × 1 metre deep pipe run then this is equivalent to a production rate of 0.64 standard m^3/m^3 trench/year or an emission rate through the ground surface of 0.64 standard m^3/m^2 ground surface/year. It must be stressed that these calculations are based on the median rates of fugitive, normally unnoticed, emissions rather than losses from pipe breakages. They are also based on the median rates determined from a study of 74 'leakage decay tests' on a total of 75 km of main and as these emissions are primarily associated with point sources of leakage such as joints, actual local rates of gas escape may be much greater. The crude calculations above suggest that these rates are comparable to the rates of gas production from old or low organic content landfills.

Gas generation in the home

The hazard posed by certain rates of ground gas generation can be put in perspective by considering levels of gas generation currently tolerated in domestic residences. This is particularly interesting when considering carbon dioxide which has many potential sources in the home. These include contributions from respiration of humans, pets and plants, from home brewing and wine making activities and from the combustion of gas and other fuels. Without calculating the relative contributions of CO_2 to the average household it is worth considering the gas emissions from a typical four burner gas hob in a kitchen. This is described in Box 3.4.

Box 3.4   Generation of carbon dioxide in a dwelling by gas combustion in a cooking hob

If the hob is rated at a combined heat output of 7.5 kW for the four burners combined, this means that it will consume a volume of gas with an energy value of 7500 Joules per second. At a calorific value of 38.7 MJ/m^3 for mains gas this equates to a gas volume of 0.1937 litres gas/second. Assuming the gas to be 100% methane which burns completely to CO_2 and water according to the stoichiometry

$$CH_4 + 2O_2 \rightarrow CO_2 + 2H_2O$$

then, as each mole of carbon dioxide occupies 22.264 litres at STP, 0.1766 litres CO_2 will be produced per second.

If the kitchen has a floor area of 30 m^2 then this equates to a carbon dioxide ingress into the room of approximately 0.6 m3/hr or on a unit area of floor basis, 0.021 m^3 CO_2/m^2.hr. or 186 m^3 CO_2/m^2.yr. This value would of course be proportionately smaller if the gas generated was averaged over the whole house floor area rather than just the kitchen. However, even at 25% of the rate calculated above it is a substantial CO_2 volume liberated into the house.

This rate of gas 'ingress' into the dwelling is comparable to the CO_2 output of an actively gassing landfill. For example a landfill 20 metres deep producing landfill gas (50% CO_2) at a rate of 20 m^3/tonne.yr would be producing a similar amount of CO_2 on a unit area basis. The difference between the hob and the landfill is that the landfill gas will be produced, perhaps with some fluctuation, 24 hrs per day and 365 days per year whereas the gas hob will have only short periods of use of perhaps an hour or two at most per day and will rarely run at maximum output. The gas hob liberates all its CO_2 directly into a main room of the dwelling, whereas the landfill gas has to find a way in. However, the landfill gas might emerge into a confined space thus increasing the risk of build up of hazardous concentrations.

Box 3.5   Critical issues from Section 3

1. Can the source of ground gas be identified?
2. How should the ground gas investigation be influenced by knowledge of the gas source?

4 Factors influencing composition, production and movement of ground gases

4.1 METEOROLOGICAL AND GROUND SURFACE FACTORS

Climatic factors have the potential to influence not only the rates of production of gas by biological processes but also the rate of release of gas to atmosphere or movement within the ground.

4.1.1 Temperature

The probable effect of temperature on ground gas situations is believed to be in its influence on the rate of the biological processes responsible for producing gases from organic matter, or subsequent conversion of gases during migration from source or through surface soils. The effect of ambient temperature on subsurface temperature in waste, peat bogs, marshes, etc. is not widely reported, particularly in areas of made ground, and old shallow landfill sites.

In large highly methanogenic landfills high temperatures (to 60°C or more) may be recorded and in such sites it has been shown that ambient temperature has little effect on waste temperature at depths greater than about 2 metres below the site surface (Rees, 1980). However, old shallow landfills with low rates of methanogenesis might be expected to follow ambient temperatures more closely. In such ground, a considerable seasonality of gas production might be expected.

Since the emphasis of gas investigations is currently on the measurement of gas concentrations, the likelihood of observing changes in the rates of gas production associated with changes in ambient temperature is low.

If waste temperatures in old shallow landfills with minimal capping follow ambient temperatures more closely than in younger, primarily domestic waste landfills, one might expect there to be a range from <5°C in the winter to >15 or 20°C in the summer, at least in the near surface layers. If this is the case, it would be anticipated from our knowledge of the effects of temperature on microbial activity that methane production would cease or be at a reduced rate in the winter months but be much higher in the summer. This view is shared by the authors of ETSU Report B 1159 (AFRC Institute of Food Research, 1988).

The seasonality of gas production in surface peat deposits has been shown by Yavitt and Lang (1988) through studies in the Appalachian mountains where the temperature ranges from a January mean of -3.1°C to a July mean of 18.3°C. Peat temperatures ranged from 2 to 19°C and the researchers found that methane production was below their detection limits when the peat temperature was below 6°C. They showed that methane production was temperature limited at all times of the year except midsummer.

Unfortunately, temperatures in landfilled waste deposits are rarely recorded outside research studies and few sites have a sufficient set of gas monitoring data to show seasonal effects on waste temperature, particularly on gas production rates. This is a subject worthy of further research. The results of such a study, could influence the guidance on gas monitoring duration and frequency prior to redevelopment on gas-affected sites.

It may also be the case that the oxidation of hydrocarbons whether from biological or geological sources by soil micro-organisms would be affected by temperature. However, this process is more strongly exothermic than methane production (for instance) and so the zones of aerobic hydrocarbon oxidising microbial activity have a greater capacity to influence their own temperature than, say, a mass of old waste undergoing slow anaerobic decomposition. The relative heat energy released by these two microbial reactions and the aerobic decomposition of organic matter (composting) are contrasted below for decomposition of the simple substrates methane and glucose.

Anaerobic glucose decomposition:

$\qquad$ Glucose $C_6H12O_6 \rightarrow 3CH_4 + 3CO2$ $\qquad$ $\Delta G^{\acute{o}} = $ -393 kJ/mol

Aerobic methane oxidation:

$\qquad$ Methane $CH_4 + 2O_2 \rightarrow CO_2 + 2H_2O$ $\qquad$ $\Delta G^{\acute{o}} = $ -779.6 kJ/mol

Aerobic glucose decomposition:

$\qquad$ Glucose $C_6H_{12}O_6 + O_2 \rightarrow CO_2 + H_2O$ $\qquad$ $\Delta G^{\acute{o}} = $ -2822 kJ/mol

Apart from effects of temperature on rates of gas production from biological sources, sub-zero temperatures will also affect gas release from the ground if the ground becomes frozen. There is known to be a large reservoir of gas trapped under the permafrost of Canada because of the inability of subsurface gases to escape through the frozen ground. It is conceivable that this effect could occur for short periods in the UK in cold weather conditions but in many cases the temperature of the gas and the heat generated by its production and oxidation would prevent freezing of the ground directly over the gas source.

4.1.2 $\qquad$ Atmospheric pressure

It is well documented that atmospheric pressure influences the release of gas from mine workings, landfills, etc. (Young, 1990). Falling barometric pressure may result in increased movement of gases through a landfill site surface, off site through permeable strata or out of abandoned mine workings. The greatest effect is likely to be when the rate of fall of atmospheric pressure is greatest.

Although this effect is sufficiently well recognised, to an extent that barometric pressure is routinely measured alongside gas monitoring, it is not often that good relationships between gas concentrations and pressure can be demonstrated. To observe an atmospheric pressure effect on gas concentrations, it is necessary to monitor gas concentrations from a standpipe which is in a position at which there is an intermittent or variable flux of gas through the ground which is related to barometric pressure changes. Gas monitoring installations in actively gassing waste for instance will rarely show an influence of pressure on concentration, although an effect on gas flows from boreholes may be observed. Greater emphasis on flow measurement from gas monitoring installations might result in wider observation of the effects of atmospheric pressure changes on gas emissions.

In addition, gas monitoring is rarely sufficiently intensive to demonstrate a relationship between pressure and concentration. The recent trend towards data logging systems for gas monitoring, and the greatly increased volume of data which results, has shown some good relationships and an example of this is shown in Figure 4.1. Some monitoring installations may show a great range in gas composition due to pressure changes so it is important that the gas monitoring data set is sufficiently large to permit confident interpretation of ground gas concentrations.

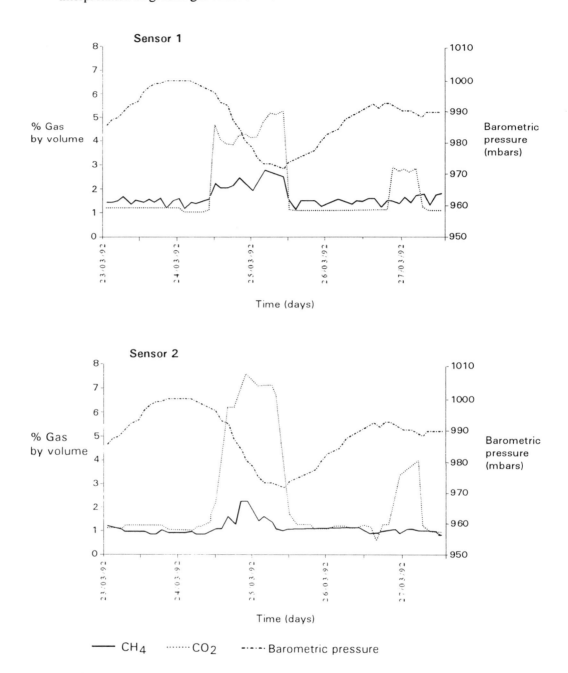

Figure 4.1   Example of variation in gas concentrations in two standpipes with changes in barometric pressure.

When interpreting or attempting to predict the effects of atmospheric pressure on gas escape from the ground, it is useful if the potential fluctuations in atmospheric pressure are understood. Atmospheric pressure varies with temperature and altitude as well as varying with time and location. Meteorological records of pressure usually show data corrected to a standard altitude (sea level) and temperature because pressure decreases with increasing altitude. Although this relationship is not linear, for measurements at ground level, the approximate relationship is a fall of 1 mbar of pressure for every 10 metres of elevation.

Superimposed on pressure changes attributable to movement of weather systems, there are smaller diurnal changes of about 1.6 mbars range at 52°N (the approximate latitude of Hereford, UK) but of increasing magnitude nearer the equator. These diurnal oscillations have maxima at 10 h and 22 h local time and minima at 4 h and 16 h.

The range of pressures experienced in the UK and the geographical differences in pressure ranges are summarised by Walton and Hardman (1973). There is generally a greater range of pressures, and pressures are generally lower, at more northerly latitudes. For example the 30-year averages between 1900 and 1970 show a range between approximately 1006 and 1016 mbars in Lerwick but only 1013 to 1017 at Kew. Full year average pressures are 1016 on the south coast of Britain decreasing to 1010 in the Shetlands.

The highest and lowest recorded pressures in the UK between 1870 and 1970 were 1054.7 mbars at Aberdeen in 1902 and 925.5 mbars at Ochertyre in 1884. Greater ranges of pressure are experienced in the winter months than the summer with maximum ranges observed in January and minimum in June.

From these data it might be expected that incidents of increased gas release from the ground as a result of atmospheric pressure changes might be more likely in winter than summer and more likely at more northerly latitudes.

4.1.3 Precipitation

The effects of precipitation on gas emission from the ground are two-fold. First, the ingress of water into the wastes will accelerate gas production by biological sources assuming the ground is not already saturated. This is because water content is probably the single most influential factor affecting the gas production rate in waste. This effect will be a long-term gradual effect rather than one causing fluctuations in gas production over short periods of time such as days or weeks. It is greatly dependent on the site cover permeability and contouring which will control the relative proportions of rainfall ingress and run off.

Figure 4.2 shows the relationship between gas production rates and water content obtained from the study of gas emissions and sampling of numerous landfill sites and presented in Emberton (1986). These data suggest an increase in the rate of gas production of approximately 40-fold for an increase in the water content of waste from 30% to 60%.

It is also worth noting that although the biological process of anaerobic waste decomposition involves some steps which consume and some which release water, the net effect is thought to be one of water consumption. This has been summarised in the empirical formula for anaerobic refuse decomposition presented by EMCON Associates (1981):

$$C_{99}H_{149}O_{59}N + xH_2O \rightarrow yCH_4 + zCO_2 + mC_5H_7O_2N^+ + kNH_4^+ + nHCO_3^-$$

The relative quantities of water (x), methane (y), carbon dioxide (z), microbial cells (m), ammonium (k) and bicarbonate (n) are difficult to predict as they depend greatly on the conditions of decomposition and the degradability of the waste. More complex theoretical equations for refuse decomposition have also been published, in some cases including sulphur compounds. However these all suffer from the same uncertainties mentioned above.

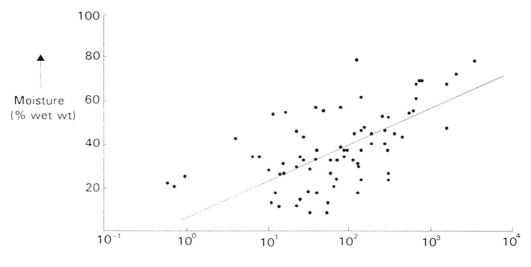

Figure 4.2 The relationship between water content and gas production rate in landfills (after Emberton, 1986)

The second effect of precipitation is on ground surface permeability and the consequent escape of gases through a site surface. Rainfall tends to close pores in the cover material thus restricting gas escape and possibly promoting off-site gas migration.

This effect can be observed in some migration monitoring standpipes and in the performance of commercial landfill gas extraction wells. In the latter, the wells perform better after rainfall as less air is drawn in through the site surface and the radius of influence of individual wells may increase. In both cases the effect depends on a degree of permeability in the site cover and those sites on which a thick clay capping or a plastic membrane cover is employed are unlikely to be similarly affected. A similar consequence can occur with snow covering although in this case, the snow blanket will restrict gas escape from the ground and once melted it will have a similar effect to rainfall.

It is probable also that in some conditions rainfall may influence the extent of methane oxidation and allied processes mediated by microbes in the surface layers of sites. For the above reasons, it is valuable if records of recent rainfall are made for each gas monitoring survey undertaken. In this respect, the model Gas Well or Borehole Monitoring Form G1 presented in WMP27 (1991) should be modified to include rainfall details for the previous 24 or 48 hrs or some reference to the wetness of ground surface conditions at the site at the time of monitoring.

Critically, in the UK, rain is frequently associated with low atmospheric pressure so the combined effects of falling atmospheric pressure increasing gas release from the source and precipitation inhibiting the escape to atmosphere are likely to be simultaneous and additive in terms of increasing ground gas concentrations in monitoring installations.

4.1.4   Wind

The effect of wind on gas emissions from geological or biological sources is believed to be minimal. However, it is likely that it does reduce local concentrations of gas in the near surface pores within waste or ground. This will depend on the nature of the cover material and vegetation on it. Wind also assists with the removal of gases from structures such as leachate shafts, manholes, etc. on landfill sites and buildings incorporating above ground ventilated subfloor voids.

Wind may have an indirect effect on gas emissions from the ground where the topography of the ground or shape of surface structures and the direction of the wind combine to cause local pressure differences which can affect the escape of gas from the ground. Such effects can be observed in domed landfill sites where there are higher pressures on the upwind flanks than on the downwind side. These pressures will favour the release of gas from the downwind side.

4.1.5   Vegetation

Vegetation on a site surface has several affects, some of which can directly influence the gas concentrations prevailing in the ground and others which can indirectly influence rates of gas production.

The presence of vegetation on a site will affect the gas concentration gradient between the atmosphere above the ground and the gaseous atmosphere within the interstitial pores of the ground. This is because the vegetation has a physical effect, reducing air movement close to the ground surface and thus giving rise to a shallower gas concentration gradient above the ground. This in turn will reduce the rate of diffusion-driven movement of gas from the ground into the air above. Apart from this effect, the vegetation will also participate in gaseous reactions because of the processes of photosynthesis and respiration both of which involve the exchange of gases between the plant and the surrounding atmosphere. It is, however, difficult to predict the extent to which any of these reactions will affect the actual gas concentrations in the soil or air amongst the vegetation.

A subtler way in which the vegetation may affect the gas regime at a site is through its effect on water ingress into the ground. Precipitation falling on a site either runs off, infiltrates or evaporates. The evaporation is either direct from the ground surface or from plant leaves after the uptake of water from the soil. This latter process is correctly termed transpiration. The proportion of incident precipitation which is lost to atmosphere as a result of the combined processes of evaporation and transpiration is greater in vegetated sites than in unvegetated sites so the percentage of precipitation entering the ground is reduced. The effect of this reduced water ingress into gas producing ground could be a reduction in future rates of gas production because of the significance of water content to biological gas producing environments. These effects of water content are discussed in greater detail in Section 4.1.3.

4.2   GEOLOGICAL FACTORS

The permeability of ground or rock can have a profound effect on the rate and direction of movement of ground gases such as landfill or mine gas from its point of origin. As such, it is an important factor in dictating the probability of gas from coal measures or landfill causing a hazard at a remote location.

Rock permeability may be due to pores in the rock structure, faults or fissures in the rock or man-made voids. Gas or leachate may move some distance underground from its source which can cause a direct off-site hazard and in the case of leachate it can result in the production of gas at a point remote from the landfill.

An awareness of the geology in the vicinity of a site producing gas is necessary in assessing the hazard from gas since random location of monitoring points may well fail to detect subsurface migration of gases through permeable strata. For this reason, monitoring standpipes should penetrate at least to the depth of the base of the landfill or to the water table and they should be positioned to intercept known permeable strata. Where subsurface permeable strata in the vicinity of gas affected ground are known to outcrop at a distance from the site or intersect with mine workings, gas migration to these points should be investigated.

The surface, 'drift' geology is often the principal route of off-site gas migration particularly where the deeper strata are of low permeability. Movement of gases through the near-surface ground will be determined in part by the permeability of this ground and this in turn will be affected by the particle size distribution, degree of compaction and the saturation of the ground. In the case of compaction, the activities of man in relation to groundworks preceding development of a site may have an influence on gas movement.

Efforts have been made to model the movement of gas through subsurface permeable strata in order to be able to predict the flux of gas. This requires a knowledge of the permeability of rocks and soil to gases, the gas pressures at source and the gas composition. Modelling of this movement of gas has been the subject of recent Department of the Environment funded research (Ghabaee and Rodwell, 1989).

As well as the prediction of gas movement through strata, some practitioners have used a complementary approach in which gas concentrations in the ground are used to establish a concentration gradient around a gas-producing site. The concentrations are then used in combination with assumed or measured ground permeability values to calculate the gas flux in the ground on sites adjacent to the gas producing site. This calculated gas flux is then used in turn to assess risk to a development from gas. Care must be exercised using this approach since gas gradients and ground permeability will be affected by climatic changes such as atmospheric pressure and rainfall in particular, so the perceived gas migration regime determined by one survey of ground gas concentrations is unlikely to hold for all climatic conditions. The development itself can also affect the gas migration patterns.

4.3   HYDROGEOLOGICAL FACTORS

4.3.1   Groundwater and leachate

The water regime in a landfill can have an affect on the gas production as described in Section 4.1.3. It will also influence off-site movement of gas and leachate from landfills and gas escape from mines.

Controlled flooding may be used as a technique to manage gas escape from disused mine workings but uncontrolled filling of mines with ground or surface water represents the greatest post-closure threat from mines as rapid filling can lead to hazardous displacement of gases from the mines which will not necessarily emerge via the main mine shafts.

In older landfills in which low permeability liners were often not required or not so heavily engineered as those being constructed today, there could be close interaction between the local hydrogeology and the water in the landfill. If the base of the landfill penetrates the local water table, as in many former-quarry landfills, and leachate is kept below this level by active pumping from the landfill, then water may enter the landfill from the surrounding ground. Conversely, if the landfill is above the local water table, leachate is likely to escape *via* the most permeable strata. The level of leachate within a landfill will clearly control the levels at which gas itself can leave the site so an understanding of the water regime in a gassing site or landfill and the adjacent land is important to the understanding of potential gas migration pathways. The same is true for groundwater or perched water in peat, made ground or infilled docks. Depression of the water table as a result of groundwater pumping activities may also open up gas migration pathways. Caution should therefore be exercised in authorising or undertaking water pumping activities close to gassing sites.

It should not be forgotten also, that off-site gas emissions from the ground may occur as a result of release of dissolved gases from water/leachate escaping from a site or from an anaerobic conversion of organic compounds in leachate to landfill gas. Analysis of leachates can give an indication of the potential for subsequent gas production. In particular, analysis of volatile fatty acids and use of the equations of Buswell, detailed in Section 5.6.2, has been used to quantify gas production from leachates. For all but leachates from very young waste, this gave good agreement with gas volumes actually produced by incubation techniques in the laboratory.

Methods are also available or under development for quantifying dissolved gas concentrations, either by water sampling and laboratory analysis (MEWAM, 1988), or by *in-situ* measurement using a diffusion cell lowered into a borehole (Lewin and Bradshaw, 1993). Dissolution of gases also gives rise to the frequent measurement of unusually high concentrations of methane and low carbon dioxide on wet sites particularly if much of the waste is saturated by alkaline water as frequently occurs in inert waste sites such as infilled docks. In such conditions carbon dioxide is often almost completely absent as it readily dissolves in the alkaline water and is preferentially 'scrubbed' from the landfill gas. A flow of water through the gas-containing ground also enhances removal of gases by dissolution.

4.3.2 Tidal movement

Some landfills or areas of made ground which are situated on permeable underlying strata and are close to the sea show tidally influenced groundwater fluctuations and gas emissions. The cyclical movement of water levels causes alternate displacement of gas from within the waste and intake of atmospheric air into the waste. This may give rise to radically different gas concentrations at different stages of the tidal cycle. However, the gas monitoring frequency is rarely sufficient to clearly demonstrate this effect. Where tidal influence is suspected the gas investigation should be designed to assess the effect of tidal movements. Box 4.1 shows the effect of tidal influence on water levels within a landfill and although in this case the gas monitoring was not sufficient to show clearly a resultant tidal effect on gas emissions, a crude estimate of the effect can be made.

Compared to recorded rates of gas generation from other sources this tidally driven flux of gas based on the outlined assumptions in Box 4.1 is very high. However, the displaced gas may have a reduced methane and carbon dioxide concentration compared to landfill gas on other sites due to the enhanced dilution by air and increased aerobic activity in the waste. Despite this, a great potential for off-site movement of the displaced pore gas in this manner exists. Tidal influence should therefore be considered when carrying out gas investigations at coastal sites particularly if the local geology is likely to permit off-site gas movement. In such cases it is important to record water levels in standpipes to relate to the tidal cycle and to ensure that a proportion of readings are taken during conditions of rising tide, if not throughout the whole tidal cycle particularly during spring tides. This will assist in assessing the degree of hydraulic continuity between the tidal body of water and the groundwater within the site.

Box 4.1 Example of tidally influenced water and gas regime

A landfill site in North Wales contains approximately 8 metres depth of mixed industrial waste which was tipped on an area of low lying salt marsh adjacent to an estuary. The coastline at this point was armoured with large stone to protect the landfill from erosion by the sea. Monitoring of water levels in boreholes within the waste has revealed a tidally influenced water table showing a tidal movement of approximately 1.7 metres in parts of the site. A geophysical survey using electrical conductivity and self potential identified certain voids and pathways within the waste mass through which the sea water from the adjacent estuary was penetrating. The waste was so infiltrated that considerable formation of subsurface voids had occurred resulting in extensive subsidence on the site surface. Although the site has not received sufficient study to establish a relationship between gas concentrations and the position of the tide, an estimate of the probable gas displacement by the tidal groundwater is made below.

If the waste contains 10% by volume of voids and it is assumed that the water level rises 1.7m in the landfill in a uniform manner over the 6 hour period during which the tide is rising the following amount of pore gas will be displaced from the waste:-

$$\frac{0.1 \times 1.7m}{6hr} \quad = \quad 0.028 \text{ m}^3 \text{ pore gas/hr per m}^2 \text{ of surface area.}$$

$$= \quad 245 \text{ m}^3 \text{ pore gas/year per m}^2 \text{ of surface area.}$$

For this 8 metre deep landfill this is comparable, in gas volume terms, to a waste deposit producing gas at 31.0 m^3 landfill gas/year per m^3 of waste, or for a waste density of $1t/m^3$, to 31.0 m^3 landfill gas/tonne per year. This displaced flow of gas will be in addition to the actual production of gas which may typically be in the range 0.2 to 40 m^3 landfill gas /tonne per year. The displaced pore gas can therefore represent a highly significant flow of gas in sites with tidal influence and although the methane and carbon dioxide may be at reduced concentration compared to other landfills, the relatively large displaced gas volumes could represent a significant hazard if targets are present in the vicinity. Ground conditions will dictate whether the driving force of rising water levels actually results in displaced gas or whether it merely results in an increase in gas pressure within the interstitial spaces in the fill. A combination of the two is probable in most cases.

The flow of gas out of the site due to tidal groundwater movement is independent of the rate of gas generation of the ground. However it is possible that tidal influence in low activity sites may promote the return to aerobic conditions found in phase (V) of the landfill life cycle (Figure 3.6). This would be a result of the increased penetration of air into the waste during falling tides compared to the normal flux driven by atmospheric pressure changes.

4.4 HUMAN INFLUENCES

Modifications of the environment in the vicinity of waste deposits, mines, etc. by man has the potential to affect the rates of gas production and the direction of escape of gases. Such effects are usually as a result of land redevelopment or major civil engineering projects.

4.4.1 Influences on gas production

Man is largely responsible for many forms of ground gas production either directly or indirectly as a result of his activities. The release of mine gas from coal deposits, for instance, is primarily a result of coal mining activities while carbon dioxide emissions from acid rainwater attack on carbonate minerals is also primarily attributable to atmospheric pollution from industrial activities. However, there are more subtle ways in which man's activities may influence the nature and extent of gas production, particularly from landfilled wastes and made ground.

Waterlogging of ground is one area where gas production might be initiated or accelerated. Although perhaps drainage of ground or rivers and estuaries is more common, the reverse, i.e. water logging, may also occur. In such circumstances anaerobic conditions could develop in the flooded ground and if organic matter is present in the form of waste materials then landfill gas (methane and carbon dioxide) rather than carbon dioxide alone might be produced. If flooding is by saline waters there is also a risk of increased hydrogen sulphide production as a result of microbial reduction of sulphate in the sea water. In assessing the environmental impact of dam and barrage schemes, consideration should be given to the presence of incompletely decomposed made ground in the zones in which the water table may be elevated as a result of the proposed dam or barrage. This is particularly important if unprotected buildings already exist on or near ground which might subsequently undergo an increase in gas production as a result of saturation of the waste.

Another way in which man's activities may potentially affect gas production from waste is by mixing of materials as a result of major civil engineering works.

It has been shown (Sleat *et al.,*1989*)* that in some landfills differing horizons of waste exist which result in part from the different ages of the waste but also as a result of different, particularly hydrogeological, conditions prevailing in the waste in different zones. The greatest potential for gas production, i.e. the most undegraded organic matter, can exist in an area producing little gas, while the horizons producing most gas may have very little undegraded organic matter remaining. Mixing of two such horizons of waste for reasons of recontouring ground for civil engineering purposes in a major redevelopment of a landfilled area is likely to result in an acceleration of gas production as methanogenic bacteria, nutrients, organic substrates, etc. become mixed. In this case, an understanding of the composition of the waste and an anticipation of such effects is desirable if satisfactory gas protection measures are to be designed.

There is increasing evidence that topsoil or surface layers of ground, when excavated and tipped elsewhere, will often begin to produce landfill gas if a substantial depth of material is deposited or it is overlain by low permeability cover material. The authors are aware of several sites where general moving of ground as part of cut and fill type earthworks has resulted in subsequent gas evolution from redeposited material mounded to depths of about 3 metres above previous ground levels. This is particularly likely with relatively impermeable ground such as clayey soils. Such ground resists air ingress and anaerobic conditions including methanogenesis can occur if undecomposed organic matter is present.

4.4.2   Influences on gas and leachate migration and escape

Changes to site surface permeability

There is still intense discussion between regulatory bodies, academics and waste management contractors in the UK and other countries over the exclusion of water from landfills by the use of low permeability site cover materials (Uehling, 1993). There are conflicting interests. On the one hand such cover is favoured because it minimises leachate formation but on the other, the resultant lack of water limits waste degradation and the impermeable cap can promote lateral migration of gas. If the use of low permeability capping layers becomes the standard procedure, gas and leachate management provisions are likely to be built in to overcome some of the potential drawbacks.

Changes to site surface permeability can occur as a result of developments on or near completed landfills. Large buildings, car parks, concrete slabs, etc. will all affect the escape of gas from the ground surface. In such developments it is advisable to ensure that adequate provision for gas release is provided to prevent the displacement of gas into surrounding areas where it could cause a new hazard. Safety from these influences is frequently achieved through the provision of gas collection trenches and venting pipework and ventilation of services, details of which are contained in Card (1995).

There may also be a direct effect of a reduction in surface permeability on gas production from waste. Old landfills and made ground reach a state in phase (V) of the landfill life cycle at which methane production ceases due to the exhaustion of the anaerobically biodegradable matter in the fill material and a return to aerobic conditions. The latter occurs as air penetration of the waste driven by barometric pressure changes and diffusion exceeds the capacity of the waste to remain anaerobic. The waste normally stays anaerobic as a result of the consumption of oxygen by aerobic waste decomposition processes and displacement of air by the gases generated from within the waste.

The sudden placement of an impermeable layer on slightly gassing ground will result in a reduction in air penetration of the waste and possibly an enhancement/resumption of gas production. This possibility suggests that adequate provision for gas venting should be made on such sites and that the assessment of the gas problem should involve analysis of the waste materials as well as gas monitoring. Analytical methods are available for the estimation of the capacity of waste to produce further gas and these are reviewed in Section 5.6.

The use of dynamic compaction to accelerate settlement and improve compaction in made ground will undoubtedly reduce the permeability of the fill to gases and may result in greater lateral movement of gas from a gassing site.

Creation of gas or leachate migration pathways

Redevelopment of sites subject to gas emissions invariably involves changes in surface permeability and the construction of features which may act as barriers or pathways to gas movement. Of particular note, service pipe or cable runs can provide ready pathways for the movement of gas, often in the direction of the structure one is endeavouring to protect. Pipe runs, which are usually bedded in aggregates provide good pathways for gas movement, so particular attention should be paid to venting of these trenches and sealing of pipework at entries into inspection chambers, buildings, etc.

Leachate could also move by similar routes and cause off-site problems, although leachate would normally be deeper in the ground than services. Great opportunities for leachate movement exist where landfills are situated in heavily mined areas and leachate entering disused mine shafts can move readily over long distances causing gas problems at distant locations. Instances of this have occurred where disused mine shafts have deliberately been used for the disposal of wastes, including liquid wastes.

Foundation construction can affect gas movement in the ground in several ways. Concrete floor slabs though not impermeable to gas will probably reduce surface permeability and deflect gases sideways.

Pile foundations when driven may loosen or densify the surrounding ground and generate pore water pressures. The effect depends on the type and density of the soil or rock. The use of vibro-replacement or vibro-displacement techniques to reinforce fill material or shallow depth coal workings with compacted granular material may affect the density of the adjacent ground, but more importantly it will provide new vertical pathways for any gases that may be present or produced in the future.

4.5 MODIFICATION OF GASES IN THE GROUND

4.5.1 Adsorption reactions

Adsorption of gases on to soil particles may result in the selective removal of constituents of gas mixtures (such as landfill gas), thus changing their composition with increasing migration distance from source. The complete removal of some constituent gases can occur, particularly those present only as traces. Different soils have different capacities to adsorb gases on their surfaces, and different affinities for the various component gases. The reaction of gas constituents with the surfaces of the soil particles can lead to chromatographic separation of the constituent gases in a ground gas resulting in changes in the distribution and ratios between component gases. The situation is complicated by the simultaneous effect of biological and chemical processes which also modify the gas composition. Adsorbed gases might be subsequently consumed by microbial activity in the soil.

4.5.2 Biological reactions

Micro-organisms in the surface layers of waste or soils through which gas may migrate are known to modify gas composition by consuming some gases and producing others. The oxidation of methane and other hydrocarbons by soil microbes has been extensively researched. This process can lead to a relative decline in proportions of methane (and other hydrocarbons) and an increase in carbon dioxide. A blend of methane and oxygen is required for aerobic methane oxidation to proceed although oxygen concentrations can be much lower than the 20.9% present in air. Current understanding of the rates of methanogenesis and methane oxidation suggests that in landfills in which conditions in the surface cover layers are conducive to biological methane oxidation, such processes can lead to the total removal of methane from the gas stream before it reaches the ground surface (Wyman, 1994).

Figure 4.3 shows the transformation in gas composition which can result from microbial activity in landfill cover soils. Similar processes can proceed in soils subject to lateral movement of methane-rich gases.

The gas transformations shown in Figure 4.3 prompt questions regarding the value of gas concentration measurements from standpipes penetrating beneath the zone of bacterial activity for purposes of assessing risk to surface structures. Such monitoring installations effectively allow the gas to by-pass the soil processes occurring in the upper soil layers so concentrations of gas in standpipes rarely reflect concentrations emerging from the ground surface.

Biological methane oxidation can not only result in changes in the proportions of the constituent gases in a ground gas but also to variation in the ratios of the isotopes of carbon and hydrogen present. This is a result of the preferential diffusion of gases containing the lighter isotopes between the soil gas phase and the aqueous phase in which the bacteria occur.

Other aerobic microbiological reactions which can occur are the oxidation of other hydrocarbons, (except perhaps certain xenobiotic compounds which bacteria are unable to degrade), and hydrogen sulphide and hydrogen. These biological reactions will liberate heat and it could be that this heat is more important in detection of gas migration pathways by infra-red aerial thermography than the temperature of the gas itself at source.

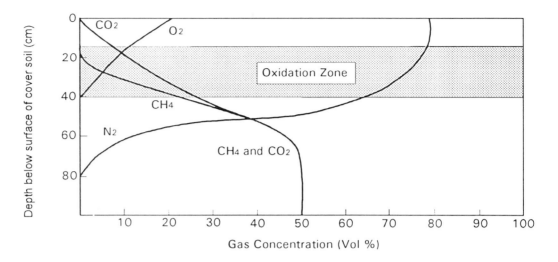

Figure 4.3 Schematic diagram to illustrate gas composition in landfill cover soil, in the absence of a low permeability cap, as influenced by methane oxidation (adapted from Hoeks, 1983).

Nitrogen, usually present as a gas derived from the atmosphere rather than being produced in quantity from any of the sources discussed in Section 3, can also be removed in the surface layers of the ground. This can be a result of microbial nitrogen fixation by bacteria acting in symbiotic association with leguminous plants in the surface vegetation.

4.5.3 Chemical reactions

Chemical reactions in soil can alter gas composition during the passage of gas through soils. Such reactions include dissolution of gases in soil water and the removal of acidic gases such as hydrogen sulphide and carbon dioxide by reaction with alkaline materials such as carbonates, cementitious materials, slags and ashes. Hydrogen sulphide will react with most metals whether present as the metal itself or as dissolved salts; and the gas itself or the sulphides formed may react with any oxygen present. Hydrogen sulphide reacts directly with oxygen in air to form elemental sulphur and water. These reactions again modify migrating gas composition but the extent of this very much depends on the chemical composition of the medium through which the gases are moving. Selective dissolution of gases is often observed in sites affected by high groundwater tables where carbon dioxide can be almost completely removed from the ground gas as it is extremely soluble in water, particularly if the latter is somewhat alkaline and the gas is under some pressure. This gives rise to the observation of very high methane concentrations in excess of 90% in some landfill or made ground situations.

Box 4.2 Critical issues from Section 4

1. What natural or human factors will influence ground gas behaviour?
2. Does the measurement and monitoring programme employed satisfactorily address these variables such that a reliable interpretation and risk assessment can be made?

5 Ground gas measurements

The types of measurement employed in the study of ground gas situations depend on the level of interpretation required and the particular circumstances of the site under investigation.

A higher level of interpretation will incur greater investigation costs and this may not be warranted by the prevailing reasons for the investigation. Consequently the methods would not all be used routinely in every investigation; some have only been used in research studies of gas production and, as such, can only be undertaken by specialist laboratories.

In order to sufficiently assess risk from ground gases it is often necessary to do more than simply measure gas concentrations. However, the use and interpretation of other measurements is often poorly understood because the available methods are poorly documented or not well understood or appreciated. There is also confusion over the use and interpretation of the results obtained because there is little guidance available despite a considerable body of experience in some areas.

This Section attempts to clarify some of the gas investigation methods, the units of measurement and the interpretation of results.

5.1 GROUND GAS COMPOSITION

This is the only type of measurement that is routinely made in all ground gas investigations. Composition is determined by measurement of the concentrations of some of the component gases in the ground. Measurements may be made with field instruments or by sampling and subsequent analysis in the laboratory. The instrumentation available for field measurement of gas concentrations has been recently reviewed (Crowhurst and Manchester, 1993). Most portable instruments have limitations when used to measure ground gas concentrations, and the operator should be aware of these when taking measurements and interpreting the results. For this reason, it is recommended in WMP 27 (DoE, 1991) that the results of field measurements with portable meters are confirmed by other, more reliable, laboratory methods such as gas chromatography.

The most common form of error in the interpretation of site conditions which results from the use of field instruments arises from the failure of some instruments to discriminate between different flammable gases or vapours; either from inability to detect, disproportionate response to hydrogen, or from interferences by environmental factors such as gas pressure, condensation or presence or absence of other gases.

The measurement of gas concentrations to define gas composition is fundamental to the investigation of gas-affected ground since it is, in part, the concentrations which govern the hazards of asphyxiation, explosion or toxicity. However, it is difficult to infer from ground gas concentrations what concentrations might occur at the ground surface or in structures within or upon the ground. In order to assess the risk in these circumstances, volumes as well as concentrations of gas have to be measured and this is where some of the following techniques can be employed to supplement the basic measurements of individual gas concentrations.

Apart from the analysis of the principal gases found in the ground, i.e. H_2, O_2, N_2, CH_4, CO_2 and perhaps H_2S, laboratory methods can be employed to study further the gas composition in order to provide information relating to its source. The main techniques are the study of the trace gases present in the ground gas sample using analytical techniques such as gas chromatography (GC) or gas chromatography-mass spectrometry (GC-MS) and the study of the carbon and hydrogen isotope ratios using mass spectrometry (see Section 3.2).

Analysis of the trace gases may reveal a host of complex organic molecules, many of them chlorinated hydrocarbons or aromatic compounds which are indicative that the gas is almost certainly derived from a waste deposit. A comprehensive list of the compounds of this nature that may be detected in landfill gas is provided in WMP 26 (DoE, 1986). However, absence of these compounds does not necessarily suggest that the gas is not from a waste deposit source since the concentration of these compounds in landfill gas declines with the age of the landfill. It is uncertain whether this effect is due to the progressive removal of these compounds from the waste mass in the evolving gas stream (and perhaps leachate) or because of the enhanced microbial degradation of these molecules in older landfills. Knox (1990) has studied the changes in the presence and concentration of various trace compounds in landfill gas with time and has established a loose relationship between the concentration of certain of these trace gases and the age of a landfill. He has shown that there is a decline in the concentration of trace gases in landfill gas with increasing waste age and that the proportion of the various trace gases changes with time. His study suggested that the proportion of alcohols, aromatics and halogenated hydrocarbons declines with age while the proportion of alkanes increases with waste age. It is uncertain whether these changes are attributable to the flushing of trace compounds out of the waste in the gas or leachate stream or increased efficiencies of biological decomposition of these trace substances in older waste.

5.2 GAS PRESSURES

Although atmospheric pressure and other climatic factors are regularly recorded at the time of making field measurements of gas concentrations, the pressure of ground gases within gas monitoring installations is less frequently determined. The exception to this is in the optimisation of pumped gas-extraction systems when measurement of well-head pressures is used to assess well performance and pressures in adjacent monitoring probes or other wells are measured to ascertain the zones of influence of the extraction wells.

Typically, electronic micro-manometers are employed to measure the pressure in the borehole or standpipe relative to atmospheric pressure. Pressures as high as 250 mm H_2O (2.5 kPa) may be recorded in some boreholes on actively gassing landfills, although detectable pressures (>0.25 mm H_2O) are rarely recorded outside the limits of the waste. Measurement of pressures below 0.25 mm H_2O are usually impossible in field conditions and pressures below 1 mm H_2O are difficult, if not impossible to measure if there is any wind.

Gas pressures in coal seams reflect the hydrostatic pressure in the strata and consequently much higher pressures are found. However, these gas pressures are unlikely to exist in the mine shafts themselves or in gas escaping to the ground surface. Pressures as high as 5 MPa have been recorded in coal seams.

It is surprising that more interest has not been taken in pressure measurements within bodies of waste or gassing ground, as it is ultimately gas pressure, diffusion and, perhaps, convection which cause horizontal or vertical movement of ground gases. As with many types of measurement, it is probably the difficulty in interpreting the results and the absence of guidance in the technical literature which has limited the recording of gas pressures.

When measuring gas pressures in standpipes in the ground it should not be overlooked that the removal of gas for other purposes such as gas concentration measurement will affect the pressure in the installation, particularly if the pressure is not great and the flow of gas into the standpipe is low. Comments on the order of sampling and measurement procedures are included in Section 6.2.

5.3   GAS FLOWS

The term gas flow is used to refer to both the volumes of gas emanating from a well or standpipe in the ground or the movement of gas through a permeable medium such as the ground. Flows from boreholes or the gas velocity leaving such an installation are sometimes referred to as emission rates (Pecksen, 1985) but this term is often confused with measurements of gas escape from the ground on a unit area basis. In this report, emission rate is taken to describe the escape of a gas volume from a unit area of ground surface.

The term gas flow should refer to a volume of gas per unit time which is escaping from a monitoring installation point or passing through a zone of ground. The location and circumstances of the flow measurement should be defined if the measurement is to be at all interpretable. In addition the gas pressure and temperature should preferably be recorded as well as the gas composition so that the actual quantity of methane, for example, in the gas flow can be determined. Details recorded should include the installation design and pipe dimensions, duration of flow measurement and whether the installation was closed or open prior to making the measurement.

Gas flows can be measured from standpipes and boreholes using hot wire anemometers, rotating vane anemometers, pitot tubes or orifice plate/constricted tube systems. These methods measure gas velocity ($m.s^{-1}$) which, in conjunction with pipe dimensions, can be used to calculate the flows of gas ($m^3.s^{-1}$) from monitoring installations. Bubble meters or rotameter-type flow meters can also be used to measure flows directly from these installations. Ultrasonic flowmeters are sometimes used for flow measurement in gas pumping trials. Flow measurements from standpipes and boreholes may be at scarcely detectable levels in some installations, (despite the presence of gas) up to flows of several m^3/h without pumping on some actively gassing landfills. Flows in the range 0.01 litres/h to 5 litres/min are typically encountered on gassing ground where measurable flows exist, but these may decline to immeasurable levels very rapidly on venting the gas to atmosphere.

Flow measurements may be used to estimate a gas generation rate or to indicate gas flows from fissures or other discontinuities in the ground. Although flow and concentration measurements are better than gas concentration measurements alone in determining risk associated with gas from the ground, flow measurements suffer because the volume or area of waste or ground from which the measured gas flow is being liberated is not known. Pecksen (1985) assumed a cylindrical zone of influence of 1.78 m as the volume of ground from which his measured gas flows were calculated. He then used a simple classification of gas velocities measured from a standard 50 mm diameter standpipe as a method of ranking the gas-producing activity of sites and assigning appropriate gas protection measures. The danger with this approach is that the zone of influence of each installation is not constant and can vary under changing climatic conditions. It will depend on ground conditions and standpipe installation design. Pecksen compensated for this uncertainty by assuming what he felt to be a low radius of influence so that when gas velocity measurements were converted into volumes of gas per unit area or volume of ground there was a tendency to overestimate the true areal or ground volume related gas production rates.

Some consultants have tried to estimate flow rates through the ground surrounding landfills by using methane concentration contours obtained from spiking surveys. While this technique may provide a way of predicting gas flow rates from the ground, it does not necessarily indicate the flows of gas from the source ground, e.g. a landfill. It is more likely to reflect the permeability of the ground through which the gas is migrating. Estimations of the flows of gas through ground by mathematical modelling techniques provide a useful means of risk assessment for land adjacent to landfills. However, practitioners using such methods put a heavy reliance on spiking survey data as it is the only way of obtaining sufficient data at reasonable cost. A considerable quantity of data is needed to generate reliable contours. A 12.5 metre grid has been suggested by one consultee as a suitable sampling density to give a sufficient quantity of information using this method. The accuracy of predicting gas flows through the ground in this manner is questionable since there is a heavy reliance on assumptions of ground permeability and other environmental factors coupled with the limitations of spiking techniques discussed in Section 6.1.1.

5.4   SURFACE EMISSION RATES

The term emission rate is sometimes used to describe gas flows from boreholes and other monitoring installations. These parameters are better termed gas flows or gas velocities as appropriate (see Section 5.3) or perhaps well gas flow or well gas velocity to make clear the exact circumstances of the measurement. It is better to reserve the term emission rate or surface emission rate to describe the actual escape of gas from the ground surface to atmosphere i.e. a volume of gas per unit time per unit of ground surface area.

The only available technique which directly measures a surface emission rate as defined above is the flux box technique, the details of which are described elsewhere (Lytwynshyn et al., 1982). This technique measures quantity of gas entering a box placed over the ground surface, the area of measurement being defined by the box dimensions, and assumes that the conditions created and maintained in the box do not influence the emission of gas from the ground itself. This is usually achieved by pumping a small flow out of the flux box and recording the gas flow and methane or carbon dioxide concentration in the pumped gas stream when equilibrium gas concentration is reached. Almost certainly there is some effect because of the absence of wind over the ground surface covered by the box and the alteration of the gas concentration gradient in the atmosphere above the ground. These effects will alter the emission of gas by diffusion. The protocol for carrying out flux box measurements should be designed to minimise such effects.

Pressure-driven emission through the site surface should not be affected by the apparatus provided that pressure in the flux box is maintained close to ambient atmospheric pressure. As a result the technique might be expected to give a good approximation to actual surface emission rates depending on the heterogeneity of the ground. Emissions from landfill site surfaces with cracks and fissures would suggest that a larger apparatus or repeat testing is needed to give a reliable assessment of surface emission rates. A recent publication (Cooper et al., 1993b) advises that flux boxes should be at least $2 \, \text{m}^2$ in cross-sectional area with a volume of 0.5m^3.

In planning applications for development on gas-affected land, domestic housing with gardens is often resisted by regulatory authorities because of the risk to sheds and greenhouses even though the houses themselves may have been adequately protected from gas ingress. This could be a strong reason for conducting flux box type emission rate tests on a similar scale to that of a typical shed or greenhouse.

Some other techniques may be used to estimate a surface emission rate, but they rely on the conversion of atmospheric gas concentrations or gas flows from boreholes, etc. into an emission rate by using certain assumptions or modelling techniques. In the case of laser-based systems such as DIAL or LIDAR described elsewhere (Partridge and Curtis, 1986), measurement of gases in the atmosphere by absorption of the laser beam energy over long distances can be used to estimate methane concentrations in the atmosphere above a site and the flux of gas from the site can be determined if records of air movement, etc. are made at the same time. From the site area an average surface emission rate can then be calculated.

Measurements of gas flows from in-ground installations such as standpipes can only be converted into a surface emission rate if assumptions are made about the zone of influence of the monitoring installation from which the gas flow has been measured or efforts are made to determine this.

The zone of influence of a borehole, standpipe or other monitoring installation may be defined as the volume of waste or ground from which the gas flows emanating from the monitoring installation have been derived. This volume will vary between similar monitoring installations on different sites and according to climatic conditions and aspects of the management of the installation. The zone of influence is sometimes referred to as a radius of influence on the assumption that the volume of waste is cylindrical with the well at the centre.

Zones of influence will be determined by the rate of gas production of the ground or waste, the permeability and compaction of the waste, the permeability of the site capping, the design of the monitoring installation, the resistance to gas escape from the well headworks and, in the case of commercial gas extraction wells, the suction applied at the wellhead.

When calculating a surface emission rate from a gas flow it is assumed that the gas flow measured from the monitoring installation would otherwise emerge from the site surface area relevant to the zone of influence. In most cases, there will be a portion of the gas which escapes via the borehole under venting conditions and a portion which still escapes through the site surface, so estimates of surface emission rates by such means are of debatable accuracy. For safety reasons, practitioners using this technique have tended to underestimate the zone of influence as detailed in Section 5.3 and thus overestimate the surface emission rate.

The same reservations apply to gas flows determined by the measurement of gas build-up in boreholes after purging with inert gas. These so-called recirculation techniques are summarised elsewhere (Crowhurst and Manchester, 1993). One of the problems with recirculation techniques is the problem of knowing the effective gas volume of the installation since this is normally composed of a standpipe within a gravel pack. The extent to which the voidage within the gravel surround is purged is a subject of some uncertainty and will affect the calculation of gas volume.

Evidence of gas emission can also be obtained by aerial thermography or false colour infra-red photography, but both techniques can only give a qualitative picture of the relative distribution and movement of gases through the surface soils of the ground.

These techniques have value in the initial screening of a site for indications of the principal areas of gas escape and movement, but, in order to quantify surface emission rates, subsequent flux box measurements at the site surface or the use of laser techniques would be preferable.

5.5 GAS GENERATION RATES

Gas generation rates from bodies of made ground, landfills, peat or marshy ground are not often determined because of the cost or limited confidence and experience to date with the techniques available. This is a weakness since the rate of gas production (the amount of gas produced per unit mass or volume per unit time) must be a primary term in the calculation of risk from gas-emitting sites, for quantifying gas volumes available for commercial utilisation or for understanding the processes of gas production for scientific research.

5.5.1 Gas pumping tests

The activity in which the determination of gas generation rates has been most widely adopted is in the assessment of landfill sites for commercial landfill gas exploitation, generally by gas pumping tests to quantify extractable gas volumes from boreholes within a body of waste. Often, pumping is carried out only from one well and the radius of influence of the well under suction is not measured. This results in the measurement of a gas flow (sometimes referred to as the well yield) from the pumped borehole which can be converted to a gas generation rate if an assumption about the zone of influence is made and the depth of waste is known. The radius of influence is dependent on the suction applied at the well head and the prevailing ground conditions, but is typically in the range 30 to 60 m under stable extraction conditions.

In more intensive studies the radius of influence is measured by the change in pressure and sometimes gas composition in monitoring probes set in the waste at distances from the pumped well. Pressures in these probes prior to pumping of gas (static pressures) and during pumping at different rates (i.e. well-head suctions) are monitored to detect an influence on probe pressures resulting from the suction applied to the pumped well.

Pumping tests may take several weeks in order for a steady flow of gas to be established. The objective is to determine a rate of gas extraction in balance with the rate of production from the waste volume within the zone of influence of the pumped well. At excessively high extraction rates, the gas will be diluted with air entering the waste through the site surface. In some cases the volumes of air drawn into the waste may bring about a decline in gas production from the waste because of the disruption to the anaerobic conditions essential for methanogenic activity.

The volume of waste from which the gas is being drawn can then be estimated from pumping test data, usually by calculating a cylindrical volume of waste of depth equal to the depth of the fill or the extraction well and radius equivalent to that at which an influence from the pumped well was recorded.

In reality, the volume of waste from which the gas is recovered is unlikely to be cylindrical since wells may have different radii of influence in different directions and at different depths. Also, there is likely to be a zone of good gas recovery close to the well where negative (relative to atmospheric) pressures are detected and a zone of partial recovery further away from the pumped well typically showing reduced positive pressures in the monitoring probes compared to the static pressures (see Figure 5.1).

In practice, the zones of influence of gas extraction wells should overlap to give good gas recovery and this is particularly important if gas migration control is the primary function. In such cases well spacing might be at 15 to 30 m centres compared to 80 m to 100 m for many commercial gas extraction wells.

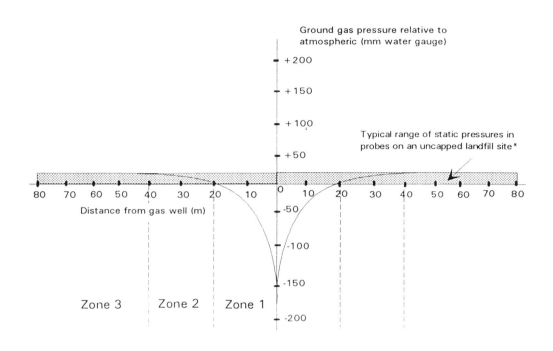

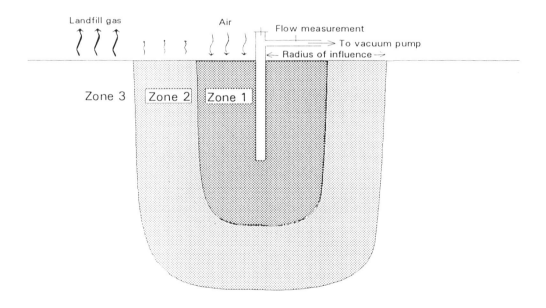

Zone 1 – Good recovery of gas, negative pressures relative to atmospheric and some air drawn into waste and gas stream.

Zone 2 – Some gas recovery, reduced positive pressures compared to static pressures, no air drawn in.

Zone 3 – No gas recovery, entire gas production escapes to atmosphere

Figure 5.1 Conceptual diagram of influence of gas well under applied well-head suction

Despite these difficulties in quantifying the waste volume, gas pumping tests are valuable as they are based on the response of perhaps 50 000 m³ of waste. This is a scale employed by few other test methods and in the heterogeneous environment of a landfill there are advantages in terms of the representivity of the measurements.

5.5.2   Laboratory incubation tests

Incubation methods in the laboratory can be used to determine a gas generation rate from a mass of waste or other type of gassing ground. Samples are recovered by drilling rig or mechanical excavator and transferred to the laboratory with minimum exposure to air. In the laboratory they are incubated in sealed containers at temperatures similar to those found in the field and the gas production recorded over a period of some weeks or perhaps even a few months. From this period of extended monitoring a gas generation rate (usually recorded as m³ landfill gas or methane per tonne per year) can be calculated from the gradient of the plot of cumulative gas production against time. A typical plot of an incubation test is shown in Figure 5.2.

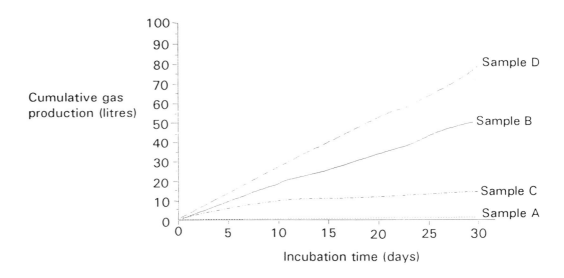

Figure 5.2   A typical plot of gas production from four different waste samples during incubation tests (after Harries, 1991)

The advantage of incubation tests is that a known mass of waste or ground is used and all the gas is contained and measured. Unlike pumping tests, there is no uncertainty over the volume of waste involved or the efficiency of gas recovery. The disadvantages are the relatively smaller volume of waste used and the possible impact of disturbance of the waste sample on its subsequent gas generation. Although oxygen is toxic to methanogenic bacteria, most scientists engaged in anaerobic waste studies agree that short-term exposure of large anaerobic waste samples to air appears not to have a great effect on its gas production. The volume of waste or ground used in the tests which have been used is small compared to pumping tests although the authors have used masses as large as 250 kg which is much greater than the sample size employed for any other laboratory test method.

Studies involving contemporaneous determination of gas generation rates by pumping tests and incubation methods have shown comparatively good agreement considering the technical limitations. Some comparative results are shown in Table 5.1.

Table 5.1 Comparison of gas production rates determined by contemporaneous incubation tests and gas pumping tests (after Harries, 1991)

Site	Borehole	Specific gas production rate from laboratory tests (m^3 CH_4/tonne*.yr)	Specific gas production rate from pumping test (m^3 CH_4/tonne*.yr)
1	1	15.0	14.3
	2	3.8	4.1
	3	2.9	5.9
2	1	10.5	16.6
	2	6.2	5.4
	3	10.9	7.4

Note: * weights are tonnes wet weight

5.5.3   Large-scale waste encapsulation techniques

Another method of determining gas generation rates from large bodies of waste or ground is the encapsulation of a defined volume of waste *in situ*. This technique has been used in research studies in relation to the control and simulation of gas production from refuse in landfill sites. The most notable examples are the Mountain View (Pacey and Augenstein, 1990) and Brogborough (Campbell and Croft, 1990) projects in which clay cells were formed to contain the waste and gas. These were subsequently filled with waste and a range of additives, such as sewage sludge, to influence gas production. A clay or synthetic membrane seal was placed on top. The intention was to ensure that all gases could be channelled through dedicated collection pipework and quantified. In reality, problems were encountered in creating a complete seal in each cell and the quantification of gas volumes was adversely affected by leakages. In the case of the Brogborough study, the emphasis has changed from containment, passive venting and flow measurement to a pumped extraction system as the means of quantifying the gas volumes being produced. The experience of these two studies has shown that the practicalities of establishing a gas-tight cell in field conditions and measuring the resultant gas flows are a major challenge in this type of large-scale study. Nevertheless, advances in the use and installation of synthetic membranes in landfill situations has perhaps improved the prospects for construction of such sealed cells.

An example of the use of such techniques to quantify gas production from the ground is shown in Figure 5.3 and Box 5.1 .

5.5.4   Other techniques

Several other techniques have been employed to attempt to quantify gas generation rates from waste. These are: enumeration of methanogenic bacteria; radio-labelled methanogenic activity tests and coenzyme F_{420} analysis. All of these have been developed and employed as part of scientific studies on waste decomposition, but are likely to be expensive and the results of questionable value to most ground investigations. Methods for the quantification of methanogenic bacteria are reviewed in Peck and Archer (1989).

The numbers of methanogenic bacteria have been shown to correlate with the gas generation rate (Sleat *et al.*, 1989) but the techniques for enumerating them are slow and it is necessary to infer a gas generation rate from the numbers. It is doubtful whether sufficient data are yet available to relate reliably numbers of the methanogenic bacteria to rates of gas generation for all types of site.

Figure 5.3 LDPE test cells during installation

Similarly, radio-labelled activity tests (in which the rate of conversion of radio-labelled substrates, usually acetate, to methane are quantified (Coutts *et al.,* 1989)) require proving against other established methods. They are also likely to be expensive.

The quantification of coenzyme F_{420}, a fluorescent substance found in methanogenic bacteria has been used as a measure of the numbers and hence activity of methanogenic bacteria in anaerobic digesters (Dolfing and Mulder, 1985). However attempts to develop this technique for landfill samples have shown it to be problematical. Peck and Archer (1989) revealed difficulties in obtaining sufficiently pure extraction of the F_{420} from landfill samples. It is also a specialised analysis technique and would require a clear relationship between F_{420} concentration and gas generation rate to be established. Research has recently commenced into the use of DNA fingerprinting techniques to quantify methanogenic organisms in gassing anaerobic environments (Widdick and Embley, 1992).

One problem common to all these methods is the small amount of material used in each test. With material as heterogeneous as landfill or soil the resulting variation between replicate samples is likely to be very high and considerable bias can be created during sampling and sub-sampling.

5.6 THE POTENTIAL FOR GAS GENERATION

Once the source of gas generation is known, steps can be taken to quantify the potential of that source to produce gas, usually expressed as m^3/t or m^3/m^3. This is a useful parameter to determine if a forecast of the extent and duration of gas generation over future years is to be made. As such, the potential gas yield of waste is a fundamental source term in the modelling of gas generation from landfills in order to assess the commercial viability of gas utilisation schemes. The potential gas yield from many sources may be calculated from compositional or analytical information or directly determined by laboratory procedures.

Box 5.1 Example of the use of large-scale waste encapsulation techniques

Waste encapsulation techniques have recently been employed to quantify gas generation rates on an 'inert' fill site. Initial investigations showed that the fill was mostly clay mixed with demolition wastes such as stone, brick and concrete. Very little organic matter was present. The fill of 3 to 4 m depth was covered by 2 m of clean clay. Gas monitoring on the site has recorded methane concentrations to 90% methane. The high methane to carbon dioxide ratio is believed to be associated with the greater dissolution of carbon dioxide in the water within the fill compared to the methane, particularly under the slightly alkaline groundwater conditions probably created by the cementitious materials in the inert fill. There is also believed to be some groundwater movement through the gravel beds underlying the fill.

The high gas concentrations were believed to be a reflection of the very impermeable site capping rather than a high rate of gas production. In fact, all the evidence suggested that the rates of gas generation would be low because of the low organic content of the fill and low temperature. Incubation tests as described in Section 5.5.2 were carried out on 250 kg samples of fill and confirmed a generation rate in the region of 0.05–0.1 m³ landfill gas per tonne per year.

To corroborate the findings of the incubation tests it was decided to establish three waste encapsulation cells on the site. These were created using a low density polyethylene (LDPE) membrane incorporating an aluminium foil which could be heat welded on site. This formed the sides and top of the cells. The cells were constructed by excavation of a trench to approximately 5 m depth around each 10 m × 10 m area of waste. The water table situated at 4 to 5 m below ground level and immersion of the membrane in the standing water created a gas seal around the lower edge of the cell membrane. The membrane was protected with a fibre geotextile. At the top of the waste a 0.5 m thick, 40 mm single-size gravel layer was added with perforated gas collection pipes within. The collection pipework was then sealed where it penetrated the membrane before running to cabins containing flow measurement equipment to record the passively venting gas flows. The test cell construction during installation is shown in Figure 5.3. Monitoring of gas production is ongoing and from the records of gas volumes and the known volume of fill within each cell it will be possible to calculate the gas generation rate. To date the results confirm that the gas generation rate is indeed very low.

From this type of measurement it is possible to quantify the risk associated with development of this land and design appropriate gas protection measures as necessary.

5.6.1 Analysis of solids or liquid wastes

There is a range of analytical techniques available which determine by various means the quantity of organic material present in a sample of waste. This is related to the capacity of a waste to produce methane and carbon dioxide under anaerobic conditions. These methods include total solids (TS), volatile solids (VS), chemical oxygen demand (COD), biochemical oxygen demand (BOD), total organic carbon (TOC), fibre analysis and biochemical methane potential (BMP). All of these, except BMP, quantify the potential to produce methane and carbon dioxide indirectly by determining some factor associated with the organic content of the waste.

Each of these tests requires the calculation or inference of a theoretical potential to produce gas from the various analytical results. The relationships between these various determinands and the actual gas potential is not well understood for most wastes or at different stages of decomposition. Those methods which quantify the carbon which is biologically degradable will be more closely linked to the gas potential, so it is expected that BMP, BOD, COD, TOC and fibre analysis (particularly cellulose) are the more closely related terms to the actual gas potential. However, all of these will provide an inaccurate estimate of the true gas potential for various reasons. TS, VS, COD and TOC might give overestimates of gas potential from wastes as they will include plastics and lignin, the principal fibrous constituent of woody plant material. Of the chemical analysis methods, cellulose determination is probably the best as in most mixed landfilled wastes, and other sources of methanogenesis in the ground, cellulose represents the majority of the anaerobically biodegradable organic matter.

As cellulose is a linear polymer of linked glucose units the equation for its decomposition to methane under anaerobic conditions, from which potential gas volume and composition can be calculated is similar to that of glucose:

$$C_6H_{12}O_6 \rightarrow 3CH_4 + 3CO_2$$

However, the extent to which the cellulose is combined with lignin for example may greatly influence its biodegradability.

BOD is also likely to overestimate gas potential as it determines the aerobic biodegradability rather than the anaerobic biodegradability, but some organic compounds such as lignin are degradable under aerobic but not anaerobic conditions.

BMP tests, however, directly generate biogas from waste samples and under the optimised conditions employed in the test they will produce all the gas from a waste sample in approximately 3 to 4 months. This can be directly measured and so there is no requirement to convert COD values (for example) into a gas potential with the consequent uncertainties about the degree of correlation. However BMP tests are still in need of further refinement and they will always be a slow test method which is sometimes disadvantageous.

In the field of liquid waste treatment a figure of 0.35 m^3 methane/kg COD consumed is used to estimate the biogas production from an anaerobically treated waste stream. For this to be applied to landfills or areas of made ground, a COD value for completely anaerobically decomposed municipal solid waste (the residual COD), would have to be assumed or determined. The potential for gas generation could then be calculated as:

(Measured COD – Residual COD) × 0.35 m^3 = Biogas Potential (m^3/tonne waste)
where COD is measured in kgO_2/tonne waste

Supplementary analytical methods such as sulphate or total sulphur analysis may be employed to define further the potential for production of hydrogen sulphide from a particular waste as a result of sulphate-reducing bacterial activity. It should be remembered, however, that the biological processes of sulphate reduction and methanogenesis compete for the same carbon substrates. Therefore, in a real waste decomposition the sulphide production anticipated from sulphate analysis of a waste sample and the methane production predicted by for example a BMP test will not both be possible in the same body of waste.

5.6.2 Analysis of leachate and groundwater

Leachate can be responsible for the off-site production of gas at locations distant from the landfill from which they emanate. This is particularly true where fissured and faulted geology permits the rapid movement of leachate through rock with little opportunity for attenuation mechanisms to affect the leachate in transit.

Such leachates may carry gases in solution or contain the necessary organic compounds, bacteria and nutrients to continue producing gas from the organic compounds present.

The dissolved gases present in leachates or groundwaters may be quantified by laboratory analysis methods: these are documented for methane (MEWAM, 1988). The significance of dissolved methane was highlighted following the implication of dissolved methane in the Abbeystead disaster (HSE, 1985). Dissolved carbon dioxide and hydrogen sulphide may also be quantified using chemical analysis techniques. Sample handling methods are particularly important to obtain reliable results and prompt sealing of samples in gas-tight glass vessels is required.

The solubility of some gases in water is highly dependent on pH because of the reaction of the gas with the solvent; and in the case of carbon dioxide a pH-dependent equilibrium exists between free CO_2, bicarbonate HCO_3^- and carbonate CO_3^{2-}. At low pH the CO_2 exists almost entirely as free CO_2 but at high pH the carbonate ion predominates. CO_2 therefore dissolves readily in alkaline waters as it converts to the bicarbonate and carbonate ions which remain in solution or precipitate as solid carbonates. The CO_2 is then not available to come out of solution as gaseous CO_2 unless the solution is acidified and the equilibrium moves in the direction of free CO_2 gas.

A similar pH dependent equilibrium exists with hydrogen sulphide which will exist in solution as free H_2S gas, or the ions HS^- or S^{2-}.

Acidification can therefore result in the liberation from solution of not only the gases present as free CO_2 and H_sS but also that present in the ionised forms.

Table 5.2 gives the relative solubilities of some of the more common ground gases and the relative atmospheric concentrations of interest from the point of view of explosivity, asphyxiation or toxicity.

It should be remembered that apart from the comments above concerning the existence of gases such as CO_2 in ionic form, the solubility of the gases in Table 5.2 will decrease with increasing temperature and also increase with pressure. The increase in solubility with pressure generally follows Henry's Law if the free gas concentration is considered but it is complicated where the gases react chemically with water such as CO_2 and H2S and this law does not hold if the total solubility is considered.

Henry's Law is defined as $w = kp$ where w is the mass of gas dissolved by a unit volume of solvent at the equilibrium pressure p and k is a proportionality constant. This relationship between pressure and gas solubility means that samples recovered from depth in a column of water in a borehole will have a greater gas solubility than those recovered from the surface. This should be considered when sampling waters from deep boreholes where the hydrostatic pressure on the water may be high. Consideration should be given to the use of sampling techniques which recover water at its subsurface pressure, or the use of 'down hole' dissolved gas analysis techniques (Lewin and Bradshaw, 1993).

The data presented in Table 5.2 suggest that hydrogen sulphide and carbon dioxide might be the gases most likely to give rise to hazards as a result of their transportation in the dissolved form because of their high solubilities and the relatively low concentrations at which they become hazardous. However, because hydrogen sulphide in particular is rarely found in the ground at concentrations above 0.1%, and is readily oxidised in atmospheres containing oxygen and has an odour detectable at very low concentrations, there are few incidents in which a hazard has resulted from ground sources generating hydrogen sulphide.

Table 5.2 Solubility and hazardous concentrations of principal ground gases

Gas	Solubility in water (mg/l) at 25°C and 1 atmos.	Lowest hazardous concentration in atmosphere	
Hydrogen	1.6	4.0%	(LEL)
Methane	21.5	5.0%	(LEL)
Carbon dioxide	1510	0.5%	(8-h OEL)
Carbon monoxide	0.275	0.005%	(8-h OEL)
Hydrogen sulphide	3850	0.0001%	(8-h OEL)

Notes: LEL = Lower explosive limit in air, OEL = Occupational Exposure Limit.

Hazard resulting from the release of hydrogen sulphide from effluents is more likely and the authors are aware of one incident in which a farm worker was overcome by hydrogen sulphide gas (and possibly carbon dioxide) when entering a shallow access chamber which contained standing pig slurry at the bottom. Rapid asphyxiation resulted and the victim swallowed his tongue. Fortunately prompt assistance, first aid and hospital treatment prevented a fatality. Death of livestock overcome by gases released from slurry has also occurred in inadequately ventilated farm buildings.

Gas production from the leachate organic compounds by anaerobic microbes can be determined by a BMP test as described in Section 5.6.1, but a more rapid technique is to use volatile fatty acids (VFA) analysis. VFA analysis by gas chromatography to quantify the concentrations of acids from acetic acid (C2) to heptanoic (C7) and the use of the Buswell equations (Buswell and Hatfield, 1939 and Buswell and Mueller, 1952) to calculate the expected gas on complete anaerobic decomposition will give a good estimate of the potential for methane and carbon dioxide production from most leachates. This assumes anaerobic decomposition by methanogenesis rather than sulphate reduction or aerobic decomposition. Carbon dioxide production from the aerobic decomposition of leachates can be calculated from BOD values, although carbon dioxide produced may remain in solution as bicarbonate.

In the authors' experience the results determined from VFA analysis plus Buswell equation calculations compare closely to the results from incubation methods of the BMP type for all but the leachates from young waste. In such wastes, considerable dissolved organic compounds other than VFA are present so gas potential based on VFA analysis will tend to underestimate the true value. In leachates from older wastes the VFAs represent almost all the dissolved organic material present that is capable of being converted to biogas. The Buswell equation is:

$$C_nH_aO_b + (n - a/4 - b/2)H_2O \rightarrow (n/2 - a/8 + b/4)CO_2 + (n/2 + a/8 - b/4)CH_4$$

A more sophisticated variation of the Buswell equation which includes the sulphur and nitrogen compounds in waste was presented by EMCON (1981). This is shown below

$$C_aH_bO_cN_dSe + (a - b/4 - c/2 + 3d/4 + e/2)H_2O \rightarrow (a/2 + b/8 - c/4 - 3d/8 - e/4) CH_4 + (a/2 - b/8 + c/4 + 3d/8 + e/4)CO_2 + dNH_3 + eH_2S$$

Good prediction of gas yields can be obtained by applying these equations to simple, readily degradable substrates. However, for more complex substrates such as refuse, the question of biodegradability becomes critical. The equations assume 100% biodegradability which is, in reality, rarely the case.

5.6.3 Analysis of coal and rock

The gases present in coal and other rocks adsorbed on to the surfaces or occluded within the rock pores may be quantified for purposes of determining the potential release of gas during activities such as mining for example. As the gases are freely released from exposed surfaces of coal or rock containing gas, care must be taken in obtaining and handling samples of these rocks for subsequent gas analysis.

Methods for sampling and quantification of gas contained in coal are discussed in Creedy (1986)

5.6.4 Analysis of rainwater

Acidic rainfall arising from the dissolution of atmospheric gases such as CO_2, SO_2, and oxides of nitrogen in the rain can result in the release of CO_2, or hydrogen from ground on which the rain falls, depending on the minerals present. These processes are described in greater detail in Box 3.3.

In both cases the amount of protons (H^+) in the rainfall as reflected in the pH value will determine the amount of gases produced assuming there is an abundance of reactive ground and that the contact time between rain and ground is not limiting. pH measurement in rainfall is therefore a means by which, in conjunction with rainfall data, a prediction of the potential gas production by these reactions can be made.

Because of these reactions, metal gas monitoring installations and limestone aggregates for gravel packs around such installations should be avoided where carbon dioxide or hydrogen are of interest or capable of interference.

5.6.5 Analysis of oil

Analysis of oil may be used to predict the amounts of methane, higher hydrocarbons, carbon dioxide and hydrogen sulphide which reside in either underground crude oil reservoirs or in crude oil spills, etc. Gases in solution in the oil may be quantified by the use of low temperature fractional distillation and GC analysis and this technique is commonly used in the oil industry. Oil field exploration companies have developed techniques for the recovery of oil samples from the bottom of oil wells and retrieval of them at reservoir pressure for laboratory analysis. Gases such as methane are considerably more soluble in oil than in water so the potential for gas release from crude oils is great. However, most crude oils extracted from the ground are relieved of their dissolved gases close to the point at which they reach the surface. This is either by the spontaneous evaporation of these gases due to the pressure drop on reaching the surface or as a result of deliberate fractional distillation.

5.7 ENVIRONMENTAL MEASUREMENTS

As discussed in Section 4, many environmental factors can influence the production and movement of ground gases. The principal ones are barometric pressure, precipitation and groundwater level but others include wind, temperature and vegetation.

In order fully to understand the gas regime on a particular site, monitoring of these variables should be carried out alongside gas monitoring work. This is particularly the case on operational or recently completed landfills where a full understanding of the manner of gas movement should be achieved before the monitoring intensity can be reduced.

Atmospheric pressure, air temperature and water levels in monitoring installations should be measured at the time of taking gas measurements using portable instruments. For long-term monitoring of sites that are continuously manned, consideration should be given to the establishment of a permanent weather station including a rain gauge, wind speed and direction measuring equipment and temperature recorder and the use of automatic water level recorders.

For short-term programmes, data on rainfall and wind could be obtained from the nearest meteorological station but field observations of site surface wetness, vegetation and cover material, for example, should also be recorded. Temperature data from the local meteorological office in condensed forms such as monthly averages, maxima and minima, can be more useful than occasional spot readings.

The increasing application of data logging devices in environmental monitoring studies should facilitate the acquisition of adequate environmental information in future gas investigations.

Box 5.2 Critical issues from Section 5

1. Are the measurement methods employed appropriate for the data required?
2. Are the measurements interpreted correctly in developing the understanding of the gas regime?

6 Ground gas sampling

In ground gas investigations, measurements are usually dependent upon some form of installation in the ground from which samples can be extracted and in which gas flows or pressures can be measured. It is the combination of the analytical equipment and the installation and their suitability for use which determines the reliability and precision of the results obtained.

6.1 GROUND GAS SAMPLING TECHNIQUES

The measurement of gas concentrations, pressures and flows may be addressed using a number of portable or laboratory-based instruments which have been developed from use in the measurement of these parameters in an industrial context, particularly in the chemical and fuel industries.

The different sensors contained in portable gas analysis instruments have various limitations in terms of sensitivity, specificity of response to different gases, immunity to poisoning, susceptibility to gas pressure variations or other adverse effects. Similarly, flow and pressure measurement equipment has defined sensitivities, performance characteristics and resilience when measuring the properties of gas mixtures. The different qualities and limitations of the various pieces of measurement equipment commonly used in ground gas investigations are discussed in Crowhurst and Manchester (1993).

In order to obtain reliable gas investigation data it is important that the user of instruments in the field is aware of their limitations and capable of recognising when particular effects could be influencing the response of the instrument. It is easy to take portable instruments into the field and return with a set of data that are thereafter regarded as accurate. The skilled field operator will recognise water-filled monitoring standpipes and gas pressure effects on the instrument or apparently anomalous gas composition results. Although some of these effects cannot be overcome in the field, the experienced operator will highlight any potential shortcomings in the data. In contrast, the inexperienced or poorly trained field technician may simply return with a set of largely valueless data without knowing it.

The accuracy of instruments is easier to control and define than the reliability of the operator. The instrument will have a certain level of accuracy dependent on the technique employed and performance can be checked by calibration against quality-assured reference gases, flow meters, etc. Nevertheless, the operator still has to be alert to field conditions which could 'deceive' the instruments.

In combination with the field instruments used and their operator, the installation or method which is used to access the ground gas from beneath the surface is often overlooked as an influence on the monitoring results obtained. Although it is commonly agreed that different types of monitoring installation invariably affect gas flows, concentrations and pressures recorded in them, there is no definitive information on the advantages and disadvantages of the various designs commonly used. It is probable that the effects of the installation design are also influenced by site conditions such as ground permeability, capping, water levels and the actual gas-producing activity of the ground.

Some practitioners, however, have a low opinion of some techniques such as spiking surveys because of the perceived large effect of the spike hole on the resultant measurements.

6.1.1 Spiking techniques

The simplest form of ground gas investigation is the spiking survey in which a steel spike is manually driven into the ground to a depth of perhaps 1 m, the spike extracted and the concentration of gases in the hole measured using portable instruments.

Use of this technique invariably means that the gas analysed is a blend of ground gas and atmospheric air. Air enters the spike hole between removal of the spike and insertion of the gas sampling probe. In addition, unless the sampling probe effects a good seal around the top of the hole, air is drawn into the hole as the sampling proceeds. As the technique depends on diffusion or flow of ground gas into the spike hole, the gas concentration measurements inevitably reflect the gas permeability of the ground to some extent. Considerable smearing of the sides of the probe holes can result from the driving and retrieval of the spike which will further restrict the penetration of gas into the spike hole. For these reasons most practitioners would not consider spiking techniques as worthwhile for any sites where clay or other low permeability material exists at the ground surface. Surface water may also interfere with the technique.

Advocates of spiking methods believe that where ground conditions are suitable, useful gas contour data can be obtained if a spiking grid of 12.5 m spacing or less is used.

Nonetheless, for all their limitations, spiking surveys offer an economic and rapid method of screening a site for high level gas contamination. This technique should be used to provide evidence of the presence of gas but not as evidence of the absence of gas. The technique is not usually used for the measurement of gas flows or pressures from the spiking locations. The results are likely to include a proportion of artificially low or erroneous 'undetectable' gas concentrations. As a result of this tendency towards 'false negative' results, results from a spiking survey should not be used to declare a site free from gas hazards but they can be taken as strong evidence that a site has a gas problem if gas is detected. Spiking surveys should be supported by some form of soil investigation such as trial pits, for example, to determine the nature and depth of cover material layers.

6.1.2 Driven probes

An improvement on the basic spiking survey is the use of driven probes. In this technique a steel tube with a pointed tip and partly perforated sides is driven into the ground, and a sample of gas is drawn out of the probe from a port on the top usually by the action of the gas analysis instruments being used or by pumping into a sample container for subsequent laboratory analysis.

The low internal volume of most driven probes and the seal that is formed with the ground surface mean that after removal of a modest volume of gas from the probe, to remove the air initially in the probe, the sampled gas stream will be almost wholly ground gas, providing the probe perforations are well below the ground surface.

Driven probes are likely to suffer from some of the same problems as spiking techniques. In particular, poor gas penetration into the probe is likely because of the effects of ground displacement and smearing. Neither technique includes a gas collection zone such as the gravel surround used in borehole installations.

Hand-driven probes

Manually driven probes may be driven to a depth of perhaps 3 or 4 m if heavy duty probes are used in conjunction with a sledge hammer and the ground is suitable. Retrieval of probes driven to this depth may be difficult but some practitioners regard such probes as disposable and leave them *in situ* as semi-permanent monitoring installations. When used in this manner the investigator should be aware of the possibility of hydrogen production from the reaction of the metal probe with ground moisture.

Hydraulically driven probes

Advances in ground investigation technology have recently led to the development of some mobile ground probing systems such as the American Geoprobe system. These systems use a combination of vehicle weight and a hydraulic drive to advance a tubular probe rod into the ground. With appropriate terminal sections, gas samples can be obtained in a similar manner to the hand-driven probes but the depth of ground penetration can be much greater. Probes may be inserted to depths of about 10 m in favourable ground conditions. The limitations will be much the same as for other types of driven probe.

6.1.3   Standpipe and gas well installations

Some of the considerations relevant when deciding the design of a gas monitoring installation are presented in Table 6.1 and discussed in greater detail below.

Standpipe construction

The gas investigation standpipe has evolved from that used for observations of groundwater. The materials commonly used include unplasticised polyvinylchloride (uPVC), polypropylene and high density polyethylene tubing. Unless protected by an outer retractable metal casing, these materials are not suitable for a driven type of probe. Where such an assembly is used in landfill sites containing aggressive leachate, consideration must be given to the long term chemical resistance of the material used for construction.

In most cases standpipes are supplied in standard lengths which have to be connected to achieve the length required for the specific installation. Solvent cements have commonly been used to joint pipe sections but since the solvents themselves can have a significant impact on the sample or analysis undertaken their use should always be avoided. Male/female threaded connections without the use of solvent should always be adopted.

The commonly adopted standpipe diameters are 25 and 50 mm. While of unconfirmed importance, the adoption of standard diameters for the borehole and standpipe would remove one variable when comparing the results of different investigations or different installations.

The size and type of perforation may also have an effect. The size and roughness of the perforations and their ratio to the surface area of the stand-pipe may impose a limitation on the ingress of gas into the stand pipe. The length of the perforated section should be suited to the specific site conditions. A stand pipe that is perforated throughout its length will provide qualitative results, but will not permit an assessment of gas variations along the length of the stand pipe. This will be of relevance at sites where fill is underlain by peat, or where gas may be coming out of solution from groundwater.

Table 6.1 Considerations for construction and installation of gas sampling standpipes.

	Critical factors and design features	Preferred specification
Installation construction	Material	HDPE
	Diameter	50 mm internal diameter
	Connections	Male/female screwed connections without solvent cements
	Type of perforation – holes or slots	1mm wide slots
	Ratio perforation/surface area	10% of pipe area
	Length of perforated section	To suit investigation and ground conditions. No perforations in top 0.5 m or more
	Method of isolating test section if partitioned	Bentonite seal, minimum 1m depth in impermeable strata
	Number of standpipes in 150 mm bore	Maximum of two is practical
Method of installation	**Borehole**	
	Method of boring	To suit ground conditions
	Borehole diameter	150 mm bore
	Depth	To suit ground conditions
	Materials encountered	Discarded or sampled
	Method of backfilling	With specified materials only. 300 mm bentonite clay seal with concrete plug at surface.
	Gravel surround – rock type and particle size	5-10 mm single size, carbonate free
	Trial pit	
	Surface dimensions	Smaller excavation results in less ground disturbance
	Depth	Dependent on ground conditions or dictated by excavator
	Materials encountered	Material to be backfilled in same order as originally present, as far as possible
	Period of time prior to backfilling	As short as possible (<15 minutes)
	Number of stand-pipes within trial pit	Maximum of four is practical
	Sealing surface of trial pit	Polythene sheeting preferred plus compaction of ground around standpipe
	Gravel surround – rock type and particle size if used.	10 mm single size, carbonate free
	Driven	
	Method of installation	Manual, percussive or pneumatic
	Preformed hole or directly driven pipe	Preformed hole preferred
	Depth	Dictated by ground conditions or probing method
	Spike holes	
	Dimensions	Larger diameter spike preferred but less easily driven
	Depth of penetration	>0.5 m depth
Head gear	Valve	Metal ball valve or pipe clamp.
	Closure	Removable rubber bung or screw cap with integral seal
	Surface protection	Lockable, steel, barrel or flush fitting, protective housing

Partitioned standpipes can be used to assess gas generation at different depths but with relatively shallow boreholes it is often preferable to install several separate standpipes, to different depths with perforations in discrete zones. This avoids the need for seals between zones in a partitioned standpipe and the uncertainty over the efficacy of the seals.

The problem in determining the significance of standpipe design to ground gas measurements is primarily due to the natural variability in gas emissions from most gas-affected sites. Large numbers of installations are needed to demonstrate a statistically significant effect. In addition, the standpipe design might affect some measurements such as gas flows differently to say, gas concentrations or pressures. A study by the DoE/W.S.Atkins (1988) failed to show conclusive differences between various types of borehole and trial pit standpipe installations primarily because of the natural variability of gas in the ground.

Standpipe installation in boreholes

The commonly adopted methods employed for the installation of stand pipes are the use of boreholes and trial pits.

In the United Kingdom, 150 mm diameter cable percussive boreholes are commonly used for standpipe installation. This method of boring has the advantage of advancing casing in unstable ground. Two or three standpipes can be installed at different depths in a single borehole, although this may require a 200 mm or larger diameter borehole. Continuous flight-auger boring provides a quicker method of constructing 50 to 100 mm diameter boreholes, but this method will only be successful when the material penetrated remains stable when the auger is extracted. The installation of standpipes into rock requires the use of rotary or rotary percussive methods.

Although there will be unavoidable disturbance in constructing the borehole, there will be little chemical change if gas is present and the response time for gas to enter the standpipe should not be lengthy.

The grading of the granular backfill to the standpipes should be selected to prevent clogging of the perforated sections and also to allow an unrestricted passage of gas through its void space.

The composition of the sealing layer, usually a bentonite slurry grout, should be such that it does not enter and clog the granular layer.

Standpipe installation in trial pits

The installation of standpipes in trial pits is an economic method of undertaking an initial investigation of a gassing site, and also permits a close inspection of the excavated materials. The exposure of the spoil to air can result in a rapid oxidation of fill materials, often observed as a change in colour, usually from a black/grey hue to a rusty brown colour over a period of a few hours. This is due to oxidation of ferrous sulphide and other chemically reduced compounds.

When the trial pit is backfilled, the material will be in a very disturbed condition and may have reverted from an anaerobic to an aerobic state.

Careful consideration should be given to the number and location of standpipes to be installed in the trial pit. Unlike a borehole installation, where the standpipe and annular gravel pack will be surrounded by relatively undisturbed fill, a standpipe placed in a trial pit will be surrounded by disturbed material. Ideally, two standpipes should be located in each trial pit, one positioned in a corner, such that there will be an interface between intact and disturbed material and the other in the centre of the trial pit. Care should be taken in supporting standpipes in trial pits during back filling and safe working methods employed where this is to be carried out. After installation, the surface of the trial pit should be covered with a sheet of polythene which is sealed into the surrounding undisturbed ground. The polythene will then be covered by a layer of spoil, to improve the seal, minimise the effect of sunlight on the polythene and also to act as protection against damage.

The effect of disturbance results in a different and longer stabilisation period for standpipes installed in trial pits, compared to those installed in boreholes.

The authors have experience of trial pit installations failing to detect hazardous gases over a two-month monitoring period. However, during this time measurements in spike holes sunk at the corners of the trial pits recorded methane concentrations up to 60 percent by volume.

Headwork valving and surface protection

The inlet ports on most portable gas analysis instruments meters will accept tubing within the range of 7 to 10 mm. To use such equipment by dangling a length of tubing in the top of a 25 or 50 mm diameter standpipe, previously sealed by a solid cork or bung, will result in measurements that may be subject to the vagaries of atmospheric conditions, especially wind.

A valve assembly should therefore be provided, which will enable the efficient coupling of gas detection and flow measuring equipment and the collection of gas samples. The positioning of the head gear in relation to existing ground level depends upon two conflicting factors. On an open site supporting a healthy growth of vegetation, the standpipes should be conspicuous for ease of location on return visits. The second aspect is the need for security against vandalism, and in the worst cases it may be necessary to bury the installation below ground.

Some practitioners favour a pipe head assembly equipped with two attachment pipes with different length tail ends within the pipe itself. This allows the installation to be readily used for recirculation tests for gas flow (see Section 5.3). In addition, if the inlet and outlet ports of the gas measurement instrument are connected to the two pipes the gas is recirculated within the standpipe rather than removed. This principal is satisfactory when employed with instruments using infra-red sensors but other types of sensor will consume the gas they are measuring during the detection process and thus alter the concentration within the stand pipe.

Soil nails

Soil nail techniques, in which a steel rod is fired into the ground by a charge of compressed air, have been developed for ground stabilisation purposes. However, using a perforated steel tube, the technique may be used to insert probes into the ground for ground gas sampling. Apart from the limitations common to driven probes, this method suffers from poor control over the depth to which the probes are inserted and, as a consequence, the location of the perforations relative to the ground. As with other metal installations there can be problems with the generation of hydrogen in the pipe as a result of chemical reaction between the metal and any acidic soil moisture.

6.2 MANAGEMENT AND USE OF SAMPLING INSTALLATIONS

The design and construction of ground gas monitoring installations is discussed above but another factor which will significantly affect the results obtained is the status of the standpipe with respect to its degree of closure between regular monitoring visits. Assuming the standpipe is fitted with a ball valve, or equivalent type of closure, greatly different gas composition values can be obtained in some cases, depending on whether the valve was left open or closed since the previous monitoring visit. This is a result of mixing of atmospheric air with the ground gas when the valve is left open. Entry of air into the standpipe will be driven by diffusion, wind, changes in atmospheric pressure or changes in ground gas pressure, perhaps as a result of movement in the water table.

The combined effects of these factors on gas composition will be greatest in larger diameter standpipes with open tops in ground producing little gas. However, in some very actively gassing landfill sites a gas composition equivalent to undiluted landfill gas (approximately 50% methane:50% carbon dioxide) can be observed even in a constantly uncapped large diameter (100 mm) standpipe or gas well. The gas may even be visible emerging from the well. This is a result of the refraction of light passing through the gas stream which has a different refractive index to that of the surrounding air.

Opinions vary as to whether total closure of standpipes is the best method of managing gas monitoring installations but most of the published guidance, such as WMP 27 (1991) and Crowhurst and Manchester (1993), supports this policy. This is perhaps sensible since complete closure is a readily standardised operating condition whereas free-venting then introduces the question of what dimension of vent hole is used.

One drawback in sampling from closed standpipes or wells is that the gas trapped in the well can stratify due to the partial separation of the low density methane from the higher density carbon dioxide. This may result in very high methane concentrations which decline if a large volume of gas is extracted from the well. This effect is most often observed on very active landfill sites where standpipes and wells contain almost wholly landfill gas.

However, many practitioners see value in sometimes recording gas concentrations with the standpipe top valve left open between readings. The subsequent concentrations relative to those made with the valve shut between readings gives an indication of the flow of gas into the standpipe.

It may be possible, using standard designs of standpipe installation and venting head assembly to establish a broad relationship between gas flow into a standpipe and the range of gas concentrations measured within it. In this manner, the monitoring of gas composition in a free-venting standpipe of standard design may be used to give a broad classification of gas flow from the installation which would have advantages over simple gas concentration measurement in the assessment of risk from gas.

When sampling and measurement is undertaken from monitoring installations the field technician should be aware of the possible influences of one action on other ones. For example, if it is required to measure pressures or flows from an installation as well as gas concentration, this should be done in the order (1) pressure, (2) flow, (3) concentration, as the measurement of flow or concentration is likely to result in a loss of pressure in the standpipe. This is particularly true if pumped samples are to be removed for laboratory analysis because the large gas volume removed for purging and filling of pressurised sample cylinders will probably bring about a loss of pressure in the standpipe. This can sometimes explain the apparent difference between field and laboratory gas concentration measurements. The gas composition in the standpipe can change as a result of the relatively large volumes of gas withdrawn by pumped sampling techniques or portable instruments. To some extent, the use of a double-port head assembly can reduce this effect with portable instruments as the gas is recirculated rather than extracted from the standpipe.

The most appropriate order of measurements will depend on the measurements to be made and the types of instruments and sampling equipment being employed and should be decided at the time of planning the field work. If the standpipes are to be opened to allow water depth measurement or water sampling to be carried out the effect of this on gas concentration should be considered. In most cases, all gas measurements or sampling should be done before opening the installation.

7 Strategy for data collection

7.1 REASONS FOR COLLECTING DATA

In order to develop a strategy for data collection, the objectives of the investigation must be clear; what information is needed and to what level of confidence?

This can be summarised as:

- What do I know?
- What do I need to know?
- What don't I know?
- How well do I know what I know?

An interaction matrix as used by Hudson (1992) can help in the process of identifying critical interactions and parameters to investigate (see CIRIA Report 130).

Not all site investigations will need to answer all the possible questions relating to ground gas situations such as the source, production rates, gas concentrations, pathways of movement, etc. However, if some of these parameters are not to be investigated, there should be adequate reason. This reason may be derived from the interaction matrix. A clear basis for selecting the questions to be answered, as defined in Figure 7.1, should be established.

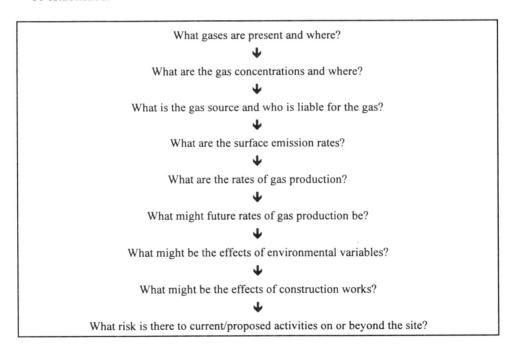

What gases are present and where?
↓
What are the gas concentrations and where?
↓
What is the gas source and who is liable for the gas?
↓
What are the surface emission rates?
↓
What are the rates of gas production?
↓
What might future rates of gas production be?
↓
What might be the effects of environmental variables?
↓
What might be the effects of construction works?
↓
What risk is there to current/proposed activities on or beyond the site?

Figure 7.1 Questions for ground gas investigations

Reasons for not investigating some of the questions in Figure 7.1 might include documented knowledge of the site area which would eliminate all but one potential gas source or the presence of impermeable geological/hydrogeological conditions restricting lateral gas movement. In addition, where monitoring is being carried out to satisfy a statutory requirement the simple measurement of gas concentrations may be all that is required.

Caution should be used when appraising documented information for a site. To rely on information sources such as previous ground investigations assumes a confidence in the work of another organisation of which there may be no prior knowledge. Hearsay evidence from current or past site users or local residents/occupants, although often valuable, should also be treated with caution. Caution is particularly relevant in appraisal of environmental investigations where specification and protocols are still inadequate or not standardised and quality assurance is in its infancy. There is also the possibility of changes affecting the site since previous ground investigations were completed. Such changes might include drainage, tipping, compaction and hard covering, all of which could affect gas emissions from a site.

The reasons for investigating and interpreting gas emissions from a particular piece of land will usually begin from a suspicion that gas, generally in the form of methane, might be present in the ground. This suspicion might be raised by landowners, consultants or local authority officers and is usually based on knowledge of historical usage of the site or sites in the vicinity, or an understanding of the hydrogeological or geological conditions in the area.

Apart from a suspicion that gases might represent a hazard on a particular site, there are conditions defined in regulations and planning conditions which may have to be met. These are reviewed in Section 2.

The objective of the investigation rather than cost should be the paramount consideration in defining a programme of investigative work, although cost will inevitably have a bearing on the scope of work, particularly prior to development of a site. However, at times, stringent financial constraints are imposed and investigation work is under specified as a result. This situation is exacerbated by poor specifications and inadequate standardisation (or standards) for ground gas investigations particularly in numbers of monitoring installations or monitoring visits to be adopted.

The investigation should be scoped in order to define the level of risk and enable appropriate mitigating measures to be designed.

7.2   TYPES OF DATA TO BE COLLECTED

Investigation of potentially gas-affected sites should commence with a site visit and review of any available information relating to the nature of the ground, history of the site etc. The site visit should be in the form of a walk-over survey which should extend to the area surrounding the site. Planning and strategies for investigations are reviewed in Raybould et al. (1995) and BS 5930: 1981.

Following this initial study, the collection of necessary additional data must be considered. The investigator needs to define the questions relating to gas which need to be answered in order to assess effectively risk from gas on the site or adjacent land. Documented or oral information may eliminate certain lines of investigation and investigation methods. For example, there is limited value in employing a spiking survey on a site with a 2-m thick clay cap.

When the required measurements have been defined, the appropriate field techniques to be employed can be selected and the scope of work split into phases. Phasing of works is useful in that results from one phase of work may indicate the relevance of a planned subsequent phase. For example, the results of the measurement of gas concentrations, usually the first phase of site works, may indicate that proposals to measure gas flows, pressures or surface emission rates are likely to be inappropriate or that alternative techniques should be employed. The range of methods available for investigation of ground gas situations are discussed in Sections 5 and 6 and in Crowhurst and Manchester (1993) and Raybould et al. (1995).

7.3 QUANTITIES AND DISTRIBUTION OF DATA COLLECTION

Little guidance is available on the quantity of data that should be obtained during the course of a gas investigation and it is clear that there is great variability in the density of field measurements in ground gas investigations. In determining the number and locations of gas monitoring installations and the frequency of readings to be taken, consideration should be given to statistical confidence in the results, to particular site features and environmental effects.

The location of sampling points should reflect the distribution of soils, particularly potentially gas-bearing or gas-permeable ground and the location of potential targets. In particular, locations near potential targets should reflect the possible range of gas travel and the space needed to control a gas plume moving in the direction of a target.

Geostatistical techniques, such as conditional simulation may be used to assess the spatial distribution of gas, the probability of specified thresholds being exceeded and to indicate the level of uncertainty in these estimates. The latter point can be of assistance in deciding whether extra investigation is needed and if so, where it is needed.

Raybould et al. (1995) give some examples of distributions of monitoring installations to give specific detailed coverage of sensitive areas of a proposed development thought to be most vulnerable to gas contamination. Random or regular grid distributions may be employed or a combination of such distributions. The merits of various different sampling grids for contaminated land investigations have been reviewed by Ferguson (1992), who favours a herringbone formation of sampling points. He determined that, of the grid patterns tested, the herringbone pattern had the highest probability of detecting a circular target.

From a statistical viewpoint, the number of locations sampled depends on the required confidence level for detecting hotspots of contamination (gas) of a given size. This is discussed at length in O'Gilbert (1987). Ferguson suggests a sampling distribution involving 30 sampling points for most contaminated sites to give a confidence of 95% of detecting a hotspot of interest equivalent to 5% of the site area.

In order to determine the number of sample points required, it is necessary to decide what size of 'hotspot' is a concern or what shape and size 'hotspots' tend to be. Then, on the basis of the 'hotspot' area as a percentage of the site area you can determine how many sample points are necessary to give a certain probability, say 95%, of detecting the 'hotspot'.

However, such confidence in sampling distribution relates to a given point in time and, as discussed in earlier sections of this report, gas emissions from most types of gas-affected ground are subject to variations with time attributable to environmental, principally climatic, effects. Therefore, the confidence in the results of a sampling distribution to assess spatial variation in gas contamination cannot necessarily be extrapolated beyond the time of the sampling. A given level of confidence in the understanding of gas-contaminated ground can only be achieved by a series of repeat measurements of sufficient number to address the effects of all significant environmental variables. To determine the required frequency of gas monitoring measurements a better understanding of the range of variation and significance of environmental variables is needed.

Information on sampling frequencies relating to ground investigations is poor in the case of gas investigations, but some information may be obtained from guidance documents related to contaminated land investigations. Monitoring requirements for waste disposal facilities are presented in Waste Management Paper 4 (DoE, 1994) which in turn references Waste Management Papers 27 (DoE, 1991) and 26A (DoE, 1993). Waste Management Paper 27 gives some guidance on spacing and sampling frequencies for gas monitoring boreholes around the perimeter of landfills. However, it states that both spacing and monitoring frequency should be site specific with more intensive monitoring at sites with greater gas production and higher risk. The highest risk is represented by a highly actively-gassing site in close proximity to vulnerable targets, with highly permeable ground between.

Monitoring frequencies for measurements of gas concentrations advised in WMP 27 range from weekly to six-monthly depending on the type and age of landfill site. Suggested borehole spacings range from 5 m to 50 m. However, the WMP 27 recommendations are aimed at site boundary monitoring for detection of gas movement off-site rather than a full assessment of a site area as would be required for a site investigation preceding redevelopment.

In general, as more information becomes available for a site and the temporal pattern of gas emission is established, monitoring frequency can be decreased unless specified threshold concentrations are detected. Where possible, measurements should be taken at times of low and falling barometric pressure.

Additional guidance on gas and leachate monitoring of landfill sites is given in WMP 26A (DoE, 1993). This guidance has been prepared for purposes of defining monitoring criteria for possible surrender of landfill site licences. It relies on the guidance given in WMP 27 and WMP 4 (DoE, 1994) for gas monitoring but provides supplementary guidance for monitoring of leachate, groundwater and surface waters. WMP 26A advises a minimum number of two gas monitoring boreholes per hectare of landfill subject to a minimum of four per site.

A recommended sampling density for assessing spatial distribution of contamination is given in DD 175 (BSI, 1988), which quotes a minimum number of sampling points that is substantially greater than either of the recommended borehole spacings cited above (see Table 7.1).

Table 7.1 DD 175 – Recommended sampling frequency (BSI, 1988)

Area of Site (ha)	Minimum number of sampling points
0.5	15
1.0	25
5.0	85

The statistical basis for the recommended numbers of sampling points presented in DD 175 and WMP 27 is not clear. This guidance is believed to be obtained from protocols for sampling stockpiles of solid materials or simply from current professional experience of practitioners involved in ground investigations.

Only for gas investigations by spiking surveys, ground probing techniques or, perhaps, trial pit probe installations is the density of sampling points likely to reach the number indicated in Table 7.1.

Apart from the guidance on monitoring frequencies in WMP 27 and WMP 26A there seems to be little other information about how many sets of gas monitoring data are required and what period of time these should cover. Some sites already exceed this frequency because of the use of fixed gas analysis systems and data loggers. However, for old sites being considered for redevelopment, monitoring over a period of perhaps two months is sometimes all that is available.

Local authority officers may have their own preferred programme of monitoring for ground gases which is required to satisfy planning and environmental health regulations. One local authority has instigated a standard for a gas monitoring programme of fortnightly monitoring for ten weeks for borehole installations and fortnightly monitoring for four months for trial pit installations. This is based on the presumption that there is increased disturbance to the gas regime with trial pit installations, which are then slower to recover, than with borehole installations. The example in Box 7.1 suggests the standard period of gas monitoring should cover a minimum of 3 months.

Where a gas investigation involves sampling and analysis of groundwater or leachate, the positioning and sampling frequencies need not be the same as for gas concentration measurements. This could be the case where water samples, perhaps for dissolved gas concentration measurements or determination of organic constituents such as volatile fatty acids as a measure of a potential to produce gas, are required.

Box 7.1   Example showing temporal variations in ground gas measurements

On one site, methane was not detected until the tenth week of gas monitoring from borehole-installed standpipes but, subsequently, fluctuating gas concentrations up to about 40% were detected during a further four months of monitoring. The reasons for the extreme fluctuations in measured gas concentrations were never satisfactorily explained, but the site contained made ground underlain by silty clay over ancient peat deposits. These strata were all in the top 7 to 8 m and presented a fairly complex ground gas situation. The water table was also within this zone, but did not appear to be responsible for the fluctuations in gas concentrations. This case suggests that a period of three months of gas monitoring should be the minimum monitoring period employed for a basic ground gas investigation.

WMP 26A has proposed a specification for the number of leachate sampling points for different sizes of landfill. This is detailed in Table 7.2. It also gives the following guidance for sampling points in groundwater and surface waters in the vicinity of landfill sites.

- surface water – 2 (1 upstream and one downstream)
- groundwater – 3 (1 up gradient and two down gradient).

For the sampling of solids the guidance of DD:175 (BSI, 1988) or Ferguson (1992) may be used as a basis. Solid sampling may be required if the organic content of the ground needs to be known for purposes such as confirming the source of the gas, determining strata permeability for gas migration modelling or forecasting future gas production.

Table 7.2 Sampling point intensity for leachate in relation to site area
(WMP 26A (DoE, 1993))

Site area (ha)		Number of sampling points
from	**to**	
0+	5	3
5+	10	4
10+	25	6
25+	50	9
50+	75	11
75+	100	13
100+	125	15
125+	150	16
150+	175	17
175+	200	18
200+	250	19
250+ and upwards		20

Notes:
1. For landfills operated in a phased, cellular manner with hydraulically isolated leachate collection systems, the area referred to in the Table shall be that of each cell.

2. At least two monitoring points in each cell should be situated away from the point of leachate discharge.

Whatever the number of samples required to satisfy statistical considerations, the work should be phased and the sampling split into several stages. Phasing allows the progressive acquisition and reappraisal of data and site information and this is the basis of the development of a conceptual model of the ground gas regime presented in Section 8.

7.4   SAMPLE SIZE

When investigating ground gas situations, particularly from landfills, areas of made ground or infilled docks, consideration should be given to the heterogeneity of the ground, the amount of ground from which the measurement is taken and whether this volume is representative of the ground as a whole.

Field techniques produce results based on the response of perhaps 0.03 m^3 of ground for a spike hole (based on 100 mm radius of influence and 1 m depth) to perhaps 400 m^3 of ground for a standpipe in a borehole, to 50 000 m^3 for a gas pumping test.

With the exception of some tests carried out on larger samples (see Section 5.5.2), most laboratory tests on solid samples are carried out on only a few grams or perhaps a few hundred grams of material.

Some studies of what constitutes a representative sample size for municipal solid waste have been carried out, although the conclusion depends on the degree of classification or analysis of the waste. Representative sample sizes of 90 kg are reported for refuse as collected (Lohani and Ko, 1988). On this basis, most laboratory tests and some field techniques may be unrepresentative although the situation is improved if large numbers of samples are taken and many tests are made. The statistics of waste and contaminated land sampling and analysis are in great need of further examination to clarify sample size and numbers in relation to statistical confidence.

The representative sample size for placed wastes will depend on the type of waste and handling during transfer and placement in the landfill. For other types of gas source it will depend on the heterogeneity of the gassing ground whether this is a natural geological source or a man-made source. The actual minimum representative size of sample needs to be determined ideally by analysis of samples of different size in order to determine the Representative Elemental Volume (REV) as described by Hudson (1989). This is the minimum sample size, the composition of which conforms to that of larger sample sizes, and indeed, the whole mass of material sampled.

The REV for landfilled wastes is something that should be determined for a variety of landfilled wastes if proper use of analysis of solid samples is to be made.

Box 7.2   Critical questions from Section 7

1.   Is the number of monitoring points sufficient?
2.   Are the monitoring points located in positions that will adequately define the ground gas regime?
3.   Are measurements taken over a sufficient period so as to detect temporal variations?

8 Interpretation and use of results – development of a conceptual model

At the conception of a ground gas investigation there will be a simple conceptual model indicating a possible source of gas in the ground and the means by which this gas moves through the ground and ultimately into the atmosphere. The interpretation of ground gas measurements will lead to the progressive evolution of this conceptual model into what can be termed a working model. This model should show a sufficient understanding of the ground gas regime for purposes of predicting the risk from gas to potential targets on the site or adjacent sites.

The schematic diagram of the simple model included in Figure 1.1 is reproduced as Figure 8.1. This shows a simple conceptual model that might exist at the outset of a gas investigation. At this stage it will only be a tentative representation of gas generation and movement without any detail of gas flows and concentrations which might be present.

The process of development of the conceptual model brings together all the 'critical issues' identified at the end of the preceding chapters.

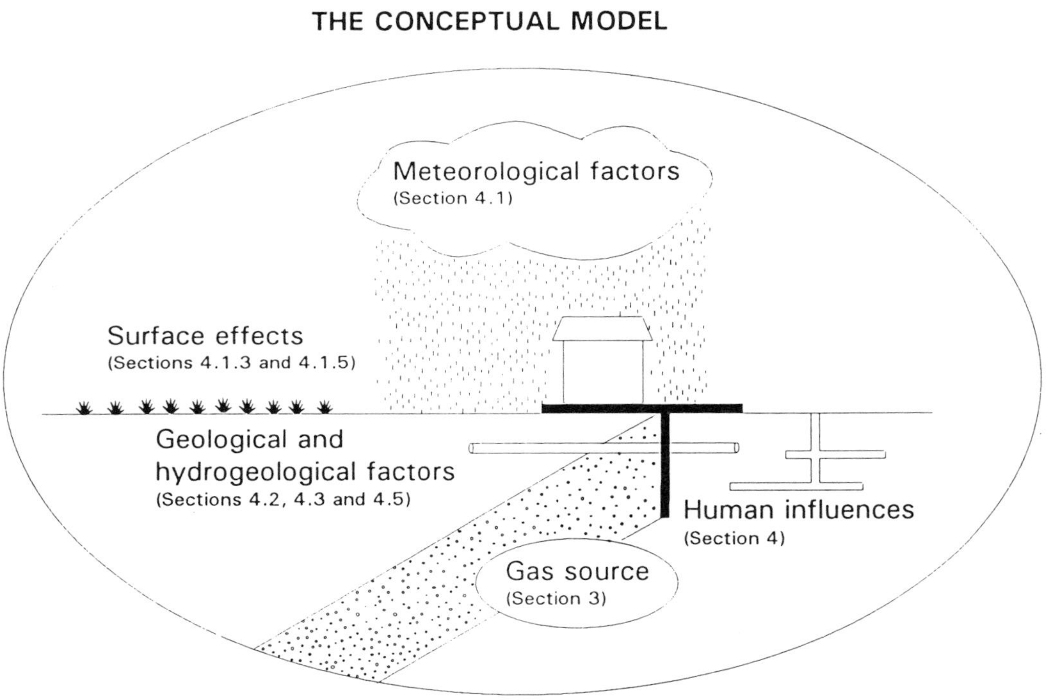

THE CONCEPTUAL MODEL

Meteorological factors (Section 4.1)

Surface effects (Sections 4.1.3 and 4.1.5)

Geological and hydrogeological factors (Sections 4.2, 4.3 and 4.5)

Human influences (Section 4)

Gas source (Section 3)

Figure 8.1   A simple conceptual model

As more information is obtained and the model refined, the users' confidence in the ability of the model to predict the ground gas situation at a specific location will generally increase. This is not to suggest that the model may not need a radical rethink on occasion when field measurements or analytical results contradict the expectations of the current model in use.

Information used to refine the model can be from historical sources, anecdotal evidence or from a programme of field measurements or sampling. The following sections describe the steps in the development of a conceptual model and show how it can then be usefully applied.

8.1 METHODOLOGY FOR INTERPRETATION OF GROUND GAS REGIMES

The flow diagram in Figure 8.2 summarises the principal activities involved in the interpretation of ground gas regimes. It contains one loop from which the practitioner can escape when he is satisfied that the conceptual model he has been evolving is sufficiently refined for its purpose. This iterative process allows the investigation work to be undertaken in a phased manner, which is often the preferred method of investigation. It allows for continual re-appraisal of information and the necessary evolution and refinement of the conceptual model which represents the total understanding of the behaviour of ground gas affecting a site. Reference is made in the rest of this Section to the relevant preceding Sections of the report and to the other reports in the CIRIA methane research programme. This Section may therefore be used to guide the reader to the information required to develop an understanding of the ground gas regime.

The iterative nature of the methodology means that a conceptual model is postulated at the outset of the investigation, however scant the information may be at this early stage. It can then be built up and refined as necessary. Decisions will be made repeatedly as to whether additional or other types of information are needed and finances available.

The formation of a conceptual model of the ground gas production, movement and escape can be started as soon as consideration is given to gas in the ground. Confidence in the model is likely to be low at this stage, particularly with regard to gas flows and associated risk from gas. If a need has been identified for the investigation of gas in the ground it follows that some knowledge of the site exists. Possible reasons for considering gas are reviewed in Section 2. Available knowledge related to the site could be from documented or anecdotal sources but will probably indicate the possibility of hazardous gases being present in the site. Presumably this evidence will suggest that one or more of the many natural or man-made sources of ground gas identified in Section 3.1 is within or near to the site under consideration. Development from the initial conceptual model, which can be very simple, can then commence.

An example might be where waste deposits are suspected on a site and there is an indication of the age of the waste and probable depth of fill available from desk study information. At this initial stage, a rough estimate of the quantities of gas emanating from the site can be made using predictive models of gas generation from waste, the waste age and presumptions about the waste composition and volume present. Evidence of the geological structure containing the waste which will affect the potential for migration is also likely to be available. A more comprehensive desk study or site visit might reveal more or better information on some aspects of the site.

The first phase of investigative site work should attempt to remove some of the uncertainties in the initial model created by the lack of reliable information. Site exploration, sampling and measurements can be used to confirm the depth of waste, ascertain its composition and confirm the presence of hazardous gases associated with its decomposition. The result of this site work will enable increased refinement of the conceptual model, although there are likely to be several remaining uncertainties. For purposes of assessing the risk to users of the site or adjacent sites from hazardous gases, it will be necessary to undertake a second phase of measurements on site and then refine the conceptual model further. In this manner, the model is progressively refined until it is believed to be satisfactory for its intended purpose. This is the so-called working model.

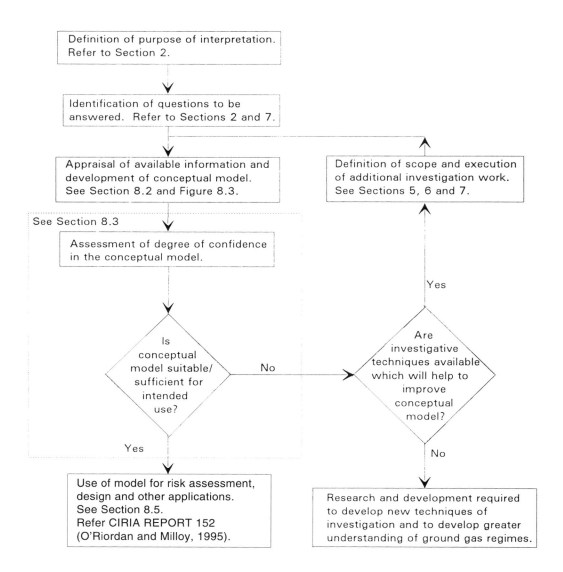

Figure 8.2 Sequence of principal activities in the interpretation of ground gas regimes

The process involves continuing appraisal and re-appraisal of information, periodic review and selection of appropriate investigation techniques, and the interpretation of the results of the various techniques employed. These activities are described in greater detail in the following sections.

8.2   APPRAISAL OF INFORMATION

The appraisal of information is a continual activity which considers quantity, quality, suitability, reliability and accuracy of data from all sources. The types of information related to a ground gas regime which require interpretation are shown in Figure 8.3 and form the basis for the following subsections. This figure shows the interdependency of the different sources of information about a ground gas regime. For example, as more information is obtained about the quantity of gas being produced in the ground, this information will interact with information related to the ground conditions and environmental factors and thus will influence the interpretation of gas movement as predicted by the model. A constant regard to the relative reliability of each interacting component must be maintained. This depends on the confidence in particular pieces of information which results from the statistical reliability of data sets, the investigation methods employed or the source of the information.

8.2.1 Interpretation of individual and sets of measurements

Reliability of individual measurements

The reliability of individual measurements depends on:

- the suitability of the instrument or technique employed, including its susceptibility to interference effects and sensitivity (see Section 5 and CIRIA Report 131, (Crowhurst and Manchester, 1993))

- the type of monitoring installation (see Section 6 and CIRIA Report 131 and Raybould *et al.*, 1995)

- the competence and training of the operator

- the site conditions prevailing at the time and place of making the measurement (see Section 4).

The reliability of the results can be improved if efforts are made to ensure that personnel are adequately trained and equipped for the intended tasks. However, there will always be site conditions which cause apparently anomalous results that may be difficult to explain unless supporting information is noted at the time of the measurements and presented alongside the primary measurements being appraised.

An example would be the appraisal of a set of gas concentration measurements from an array of standpipes in filled ground. Most of the results could show gas compositions of methane and carbon dioxide of the order of 20% to 50% by volume for each gas with the balance being atmospheric gases. Some standpipes might show very little methane or carbon dioxide present. One might draw the conclusion that these areas were unaffected by ground gas. However, results of other measurements or on-site observations could show that the low gas concentrations measured in some standpipes were due to other factors such as a rise in the water table submerging all the standpipe perforations, the failure of the drilling company to use perforated or slotted pipe, the presence of local clay deposits around the standpipes or damage/poor construction of the standpipe head assembly.

Sets of measurements

As well as judging the reliability of each measurement, the appraisal should consider each result in the context of sets taken at a similar time and the adequacy of the sets themselves. The data sets should be evaluated in terms of:

- the quantity and timing of measurements made (see Section 7)

- the distribution of locations at which measurements were made (see Section 7)

- the suitability of the type of measurement made (see Sections 5 and 6).

The quantity of data obtained should be sufficient to give confidence that the results are representative of the site area of interest. In statistical terms, the quantity of data necessary to give a certain confidence in the results remains undefined since few studies have specifically looked at the heterogeneity of gas-affected sites. Section 7 reviews the available guidance but it is acknowledged that a universal statistical basis for sampling of gas-affected sites is not yet available. This is because the presence of gas is likely to vary with time and movement of the gas is dependent on physical features of the site. The heterogeneity of gas generation is also likely to be highly site specific.

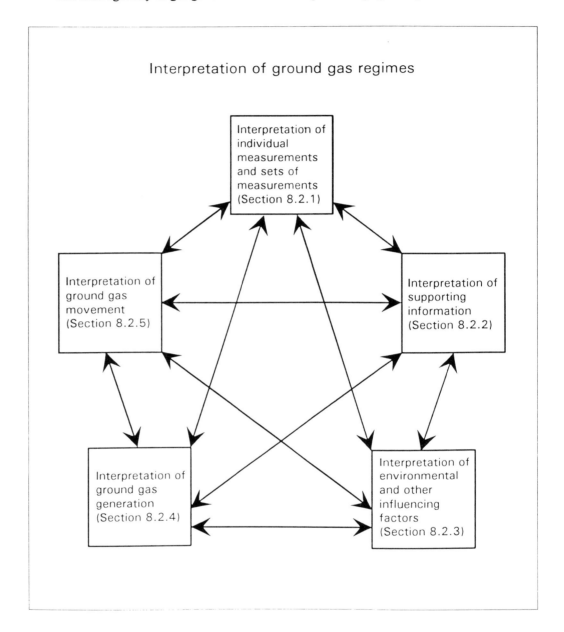

Figure 8.3 Appraisal of available information about the ground gas regime – components of a complete interpretation

The spatial distribution of the locations at which measurements are made is usually a combination of a random or grid type array of locations combined with a subjective bias in favour of specific areas where it is perceived that there is a greater need for data acquisition. This bias could be from prior knowledge of the site or the presence of specific features on the site. For example, buildings adjacent to only one side of a site might dictate that a greater amount of data is collected in the area nearest to these targets. Such bias in the sampling distribution stems from supporting information or desk study evidence related to the site. Apart from the presence of potentially sensitive, existing targets, other factors influencing the placing of sampling points could include the known limits of the waste, geological evidence or specific features of a proposed development on the site.

As ground gas conditions show too often an indistinct variation with time, the appraisal of the adequacy of the quantity of data should address the time scale over which repeated measurements were taken as well as the spatial distribution. This is primarily to address the effects of environmental variables and is discussed further in Section 8.2.5.

In addition to the quantity and distribution of data, an important consideration is the type of measurement made. Frequently, the parameters measured are not those most relevant to the reasons for undertaking the ground gas investigation. A common example of this is the simple measurement of gas concentrations when the reason for the investigation is a proposed building development on the site. An assessment of risk from gas to the proposed development is required and perhaps the design of protective measures. Gas concentration data is of limited value to either of these objectives. Instead, a measurement relating to the volumes (as well as the concentration) of hazardous gases being produced from the ground should be made. Such measurements could include the determination of either gas generation rates (Section 5.5) or of surface emission rates (Section 5.4) for example.

When appraising or interpreting sets of measurements, due regard should be given to the uses that can be made of and what conclusions can justifiably be drawn from each type of measurement technique employed.

8.2.2   Interpretation of supporting information

Supporting information that can aid formation of a conceptual model of ground gas generation can be of two types. These are:
- archival, historical or other documented information
- site observations.

The former group includes information such as:
- records of tipping or infilling, including waste types and quantities, possibly retained by local authorities
- evidence of the presence and dimensions of former docks or other depressions in the ground, derived from historic maps or aerial photographs
- records of mining activity obtained from local archives or British Coal
- evidence of former bogs/marshes from old maps
- records of groundworks resulting from earlier development in the vicinity
- information on past industrial activity which might have left deposits or otherwise contaminated the ground
- information on alterations to local hydrogeology or site drainage.

Site observations during an initial walkover survey or during the course of routine gas measurement visits to site are forms of supporting information often neglected by the inexperienced or poorly trained site personnel, but which can provide valuable information. These observations may be used to explain anomalous field measurements or to support aspects of the conceptual model.

Such observations can include the following:
- ground cracks or depressions
- evidence of disused mine workings

- health of site vegetation
- visual appearance of the ground surface
- the presence of permanent or temporary surface water
- soil and rock type
- evidence of farming activities such as slurry or silage liquor storage or disposal
- odours or visible evidence of escaping gas, particularly landfill gas
- presence of targets potentially at risk from gas on or in the vicinity of the site
- anecdotal or visible evidence of activities such as fly tipping.

These observations can sometimes indicate the limits of gassing ground, the reason for gas generation, the broad scale of gas emissions and some points of gas escape. However, it should be remembered that such observations are supporting, rather than definitive sources of information relating to gassing ground, and as such, should be confirmed by site measurements.

As well as providing useful information in its own right, desk study and observational information from site visits can be useful in planning the first phase of site investigation works.

The value of supporting information to the conceptual model of a ground gas regime lies usually in corroborating other data on the gas source, migration pathways or gas emission rates. The information will usually be indicative rather than exact. However, supporting information should not be undervalued because of its imprecise nature, as this type of information is usually the basis for the initial conceptual model. Supporting information is desirable if not essential prior to the selection of investigation and measurement techniques which may be impractical or irrelevant on some sites.

8.2.3 Interpretation of ground gas generation

When interpreting the process of generation of hazardous gases in the ground, there are four questions which need to be answered. These are:

1. What is the source of the gas? (see Section 3 and CIRIA Report 130, (Hooker and Bannon, 1993))
2. What is the current rate of gas generation?
3. What is the potential quantity of gas which can be produced from the source?
4. How will the gas potential be realised over time?

Source of the gas

Potential sources of gas in the ground are discussed in Section 3, as are the means by which the source can be identified. The interpretation of gas source should be achieved by a combination of strong supporting information related to the site, observations on site, such as trial pit or borehole logs, and analysis of gas, water or solid samples. In addition to confirming the presence of gas, analysis of gas samples is the principal method of providing evidence of the gas source. However, because gas source identification can be difficult from gas analysis alone, supporting information, such as observations and historical information, often plays an important part in the determination of the gas source.

Rate of gas generation

The rate of gas generation can be either predicted, once the source is known, or measured. Predictive techniques depend on mathematical or empirical models. Both of these approaches can be extremely inaccurate if knowledge of the source is not good. In addition, gas generation rates from many of the different sources can be extremely site specific. Mathematical models suffer from the fact that gas generation from many gassing sites continues for an extremely long time and real data collected over complete periods of gas production are not available against which any model can be verified. Predictions of model-derived gas emissions, rather than generation, have been compared to gas related hazard events (Young, 1991).

Simple mathematical models of gas generation from landfills usually rely on waste input data, theoretical gas yields for the wastes and a mathematical term governing the conversion of the gas potential into actual gas over time. Sometimes the mathematics for the conversion of the waste to gas is based on simple first order exponential decay equations similar to those used to define radioactive decay. However, although this can give a good approximation to the actual decomposition as observed in controlled laboratory conditions, it is undoubtedly too simple to model a real waste deposit where such fundamental parameters as temperature and water content, which influence the rates of gas generation, can vary in space and time.

Methods for the measurement of gas generation rates are also poorly developed but, those techniques available are reviewed in Section 5. As these methods are in their infancy and not applicable to gas generation from all sources, it is not surprising that reported data are scarce.

The empirical approach is equally fraught with difficulties and uncertainties. Reported gas generation rate values for gas from various sources are discussed in Section 3.3. If actual site measurements of gas generation rates are to be attempted, the options can be broadly split into two groups. In the first, a method which determines the quantity of gas emanating through a given area of ground surface can be used to determine the surface emission rate (Section 5.4).

The second approach is to quantify the volumes of gas emanating from a given volume of ground, either by measuring gas flows from installations in the field and relating them to an estimated volume of ground from which the gas is derived or by sampling and recording gas production from measured volumes or masses of waste (Sections 5.3 and 5.5). The results of these measurements of gas generation rates can be converted into surface emission rate values if the depth of gassing ground is known.

Rates of gas generation from sources limited by factors other than reactions within the ground can be calculated by other means. For example, the rates of gas production attributable to the action of acidic precipitation on carbonate rich rocks can be calculated from rainfall quantities and composition as in Box 3.2 although the validity of the assumptions contained in this example need confirmation from field evidence.

The quantitative information on gas generation rates or surface emission rates can be used to determine gas fluxes through a given area of ground surface, displaced gas flows in the event of reductions in surface permeability or potential gas fluxes through permeable subsurface strata.

Potential to produce gas

Every ground gas source must have a finite potential to produce gas in the ground. In the case of landfills, made ground, peat bogs, marshes, lake and river sediments, etc. this is related to the quantity of biodegradable organic matter. The potential for mine gas to be emitted from coal deposits is limited by the amount of gas adsorbed or occluded within the coal, although the potential for gas displacement from abandoned mines is more related to the void volume within the mine tunnels. The potential gas production from other sources, such as the generation of carbon dioxide from the action of acids in rainwater on carbonate minerals, might be considered to be almost infinite where a large quantity of the reactive mineral is present.

Most cases of gas-affected ground result from a gas source which is part of the way through its gas generating life. It is therefore difficult to estimate how much gas is still capable of being produced. As with estimates of the rates of gas generation, mathematical models can be used to calculate the remaining gas producing potential but obviously this will suffer from similar uncertainties over the validity of the various models used.

Alternatively, direct measurement of the gas potential of the source can be made, providing samples can be obtained and appropriate analytical methods are employed in the laboratory. Methods suitable for the determination of the gas potential of most gas producing substrates, whether solid or liquids are included in Section 5.6.

Gas production in the future

Currently, practitioners of ground gas investigations tend to take one of the three following approaches to predicting future gas production:

- they assume that future gas generation will be the same or less than the current rate
- they use mathematical models, where available, to predict future gas generation
- they ignore the consequences of future gas generation being different from the current rate.

The first approach, which assumes that the risk will only decrease from the time of the investigation onwards, is probably valid in most cases. Gas generation from wastes or other organic deposits would be expected to decrease as the degradable organic content is exhausted, except in the early stages of decomposition when methanogenic activity is still becoming established in the waste. During this initial period the gas generation from a site can accelerate as more waste is present and the methanogenesis becomes more universally established. This phase in landfills is likely to occur during the operational phase of the site or shortly afterwards when gas monitoring and control measures should be in place. Therefore it is a reasonable conclusion that gas generation from waste deposits some years after the completion of the site is likely only to decrease providing the environmental conditions are not altered. Alteration of the water regime is the most likely influence on future gas production and the consequences of this are discussed in Section 4.1.3.

The second approach depends on mathematical modelling to predict future gas generation and as discussed previously in this section the reliability of the various predictive models used is unsubstantiated.

The third approach should be regarded as negligent where the gas investigation has been carried out for purposes of risk assessment or design of control measures prior to development of a site. The safety of the building or users of a site should be determined not only for the present time but also for the projected life of the building.

Mine gas emission can possibly be more predictable since its release from coal is primarily as a result of man's activities. During the active life of a coal mine the gas emission is closely related to the amount of exposed coal face and the degree of fracturing of coal during mining. Gas will also be controlled for miners' safety during this period. After cessation of mining the emission of gas from the coal declines rapidly over perhaps six months, and once mine ventilation is terminated the emission of gas becomes more a question of displacement by water entering the mine than actual emission from the coal. This is then predictable to the extent that the rate of water ingress into the mine can be predicted, monitored or controlled and the routes for gas escape may be understood.

Other sources of gas from which the future gas production may be somewhat predictable include carbon dioxide release resulting from acid rain reaction with carbonate minerals. In this case, trends in rainfall patterns and more importantly, in rain acidity will determine the trends in future gas production from this source. In addition, the control of rain water as part of a development will affect the extent of this reaction. For example, covering of a site with hardcover incorporating dedicated drainage to take rainwater to local water courses would result in reduced contact between rain water and the geology underlying the site. This might then result in reduced carbon dioxide production in the ground after site redevelopment, although the hardcover may have the effect of increasing the carbon dioxide concentrations in the ground.

8.2.4 Interpretation of ground gas movement

After the gas source or sources have been identified and the mechanism of generation is understood, the means of gas escape from the ground and the consequences in terms of gas concentrations at points remote from the source, must be determined. This requires the pathways of gas movement from source to atmosphere to be defined and the quantities of gas or effects of gas movement via any of these pathways to be appreciated. In forming the conceptual model of gas generation and escape from a source of gas in the ground, it is necessary to undertake a gas balance exercise taking into account the total amount of gas produced from the source at any time. This must be balanced by:

- gas escaping to the atmosphere
- gas moving laterally away through the ground
- gas carried away in solution
- gas consumed or trapped by physical, chemical or biological processes in the ground.

In some sites where the gas source is surrounded by impermeable strata and the source has permeable surface cover layers, the gas can entirely escape through the ground surface above the source or be consumed by biological processes in the surface layers of the ground.

In other sites, in which an impermeable ground surface such as compacted clay or areas of hardstanding prevent gas escape from directly above the source, most of the produced gas can be forced to move laterally beneath the ground surface and can emerge from the ground at some distance from the source. The gas flux can be driven by pressure or diffusion. In general, where the gas source is surrounded by permeable strata, the flow of gas is likely to be predominantly by diffusion processes, and if there is little resistance to gas escape from the ground by diffusion, low gas pressures will be observed in the ground. Where impermeable ground or man-made features restrict diffusion, gas pressures will develop and the escape of gas through available pathways will be driven by the pressure gradient between gas source and the atmosphere. Gas pressure measurements (Section 5.2) can therefore provide useful evidence of the primary process of gas escape from a site. It is likely that a combination of pressure and diffusion driven gas flows are the means of gas escape at most sites, as pressures vary within the source, ground permeability can be variable and site surface permeability can fluctuate over time. As discussed in Section 4.1.3, rainfall, through its effect on soil moisture, can significantly influence ground permeability and therefore gas migration patterns, gas pressures and gas flows.

The problems of modelling gas migration from landfill sites has prompted the work of Ghabaee and Rodwell (1989) who identified permeability and porosity of the ground, the gas viscosity and the binary molecular diffusion coefficients as the principal factors governing movement of gas from the source. The actual gas flux occurring at any point in the vicinity of a source of ground gas will be dependent on these factors plus the gas generating activity of the source itself.

The balance between the various routes of gas escape or consumption in the ground will not be constant, consequently when interpreting movements from source to atmosphere it is necessary to consider the effects of changes in gas generation rates, the physical characteristics of the ground and perhaps the source itself, and the biological, and other processes acting on the gas. All of these can be subject to short- or long-term changes with consequent effects on the regime of ground gas movement.

The picture of ground gas movement which must be developed and incorporated into the complete conceptual model of the gas regime is built up from the combined understanding of the source and the local ground conditions, coupled with actual evidence of the presence of gas at points remote from the source. The relevant evidence for defining gas movement characteristics can be derived from many sources including the following:

- geological information
- measurements of gas generation or surface emission rates
- measurements of gas pressures
- measurements of gas concentrations at points remote from the gas source
- measurements of biological conversion rates such as methane oxidation
- evidence of groundwater or leachate positions and movement
- meteorological measurements and their effect on one or more of the above.

8.2.5 Interpretation of environmental and other influencing factors

The possible effects of environmental variables are discussed in Section 4, but the task in successfully interpreting a ground gas regime is to determine which effects are relevant. It is perhaps easier to speculate on probable effects of environmental or human influences on the gas regime than to predict with any confidence that a certain change in the field conditions will bring about a corresponding change in gas generation or escape from the ground.

While the likely effect of an environmental change on a ground gas regime might be known, prediction of the magnitude of the effect is likely to be subjective.

Predictive models of environmental effects have been developed and one such (Young, 1993), developed for modelling gas release from a landfill, has been used to predict the effect of falling barometric pressures on migrating gas as occurred in the Loscoe disaster (Williams and Aitkenhead, 1989).

Accurate determination of the effects of environmental variables on the ground gas regime depends upon a vast amount of data needed to show correlations. This is a particular problem when several environmental variables may be changing independently. Groundwater levels, rainfall, barometric pressure and ambient temperature may all need to be monitored over extended periods to establish firm relationships with the gas regime.

The recent availability of relatively low cost data logging systems has facilitated the collection of sufficient data to observe the interaction between gas and some environmental variables, but for most sites monitoring is frequently over an insufficient period to demonstrate the interactions involved. Instead, judgements have to be made without a full understanding of the interaction of the gas regime with its environment. This is usually by professional judgement based on experience of similar sites.

The situation is similar when it comes to the prediction of the effects of man-made features on the gas regime. Intelligent scrutiny of the plans for a proposed development can identify man-made pathways for gas movement, barriers to gas escape or areas for gas collection. It might also be possible to estimate some of the effects on gas production at source. However, it is rarely possible to interpret all these effects accurately and in combination in order to predict the net effect on the gas regime.

For example, if a development involves laying a service trench across gas-contaminated land it could not be predicted with any confidence that a specific quantity of ground gas would emerge at the end of the service pipe run. The calculation requires too many assumptions about volumes of gas generated and captured by the service run trench and the efficiencies of transport along the trench, which will undoubtedly leak gas into or collect gas from the surrounding ground. In most cases, the service run crossing gassing ground would be identified as a route for potential gas conveyance, and action would have to be taken to prevent gas entry into any building or structure to which the service is laid.

This example shows that it is possible to employ appropriate safety practices in design even though the conceptual model used in practice is not capable of accurately defining the behaviour of the gas regime under all circumstances and conditions. Although the conceptual model will not always be able to predict effects on gas regimes, it will create a picture of the gas regime within which the effects of subsequent developments can be assessed.

This leads to the decision of how complex the conceptual model needs to be and what level of confidence the user has in it for different applications.

8.3 CONFIDENCE IN THE CONCEPTUAL MODEL

The development of the conceptual model of ground gas generation and movement can proceed from the point of first interest in ground gas on a site, as described in Section 8.1. The model will then be refined as more information about ground conditions and the history of the site is obtained and further on-site measurements are made. Ultimately, it will reach a stage, the 'working model', when it is used to describe the gas regime qualitatively or quantitatively, depending on the degree of complexity.

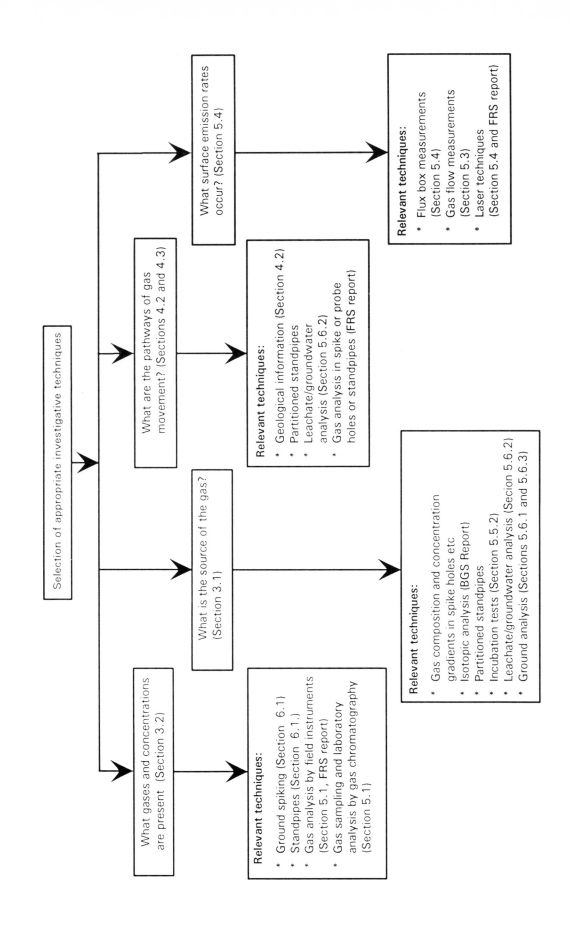

Figure 8.4 Definition of scope and execution of investigation work

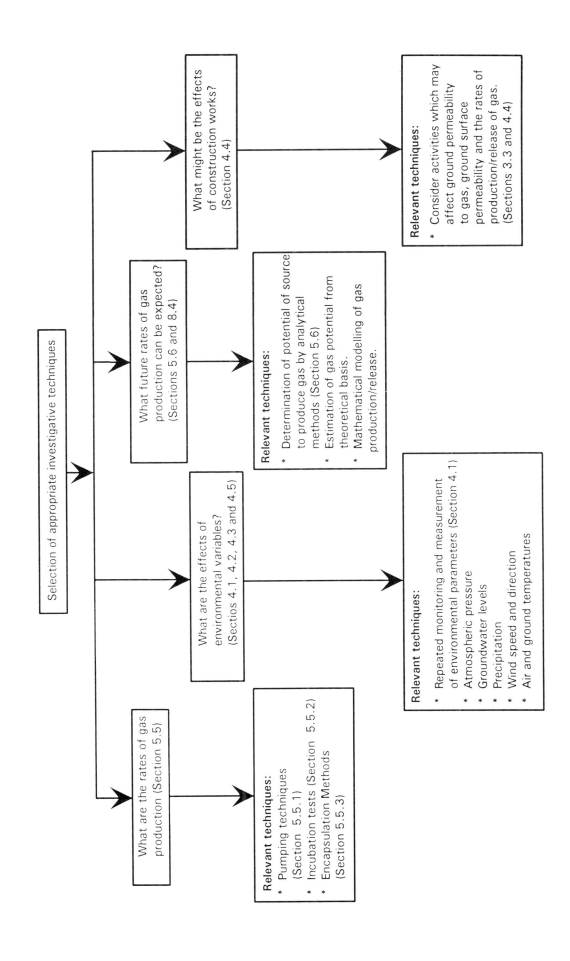

Figure 8.4 Definition of scope and execution of investigation work

Confidence in the 'working model' of any ground gas regime is derived from the reliability and suitability of the individual items and types of information and measurements. When interpreted together, the confidence in the whole body of information can be greater than in the individual components provided that they consistently support the model which has been described.

In order to assign a quantitative degree of confidence to a conceptual model it is necessary to use it to predict a feature of the gas regime. This could be the presence or absence of gas, or the magnitude of gas concentrations in the ground at points within the environs of the site. The use of field measurements to confirm the predictions made would be a method by which the reliability of the model could be validated for certain applications. However, the confidence in the 'working model' will frequently differ depending on the application.

For example, there might be a high degree of confidence in the ability of a model to predict the presence of gas in a certain situation, but there could be a lower confidence in the ability to predict actual concentrations of gas at certain locations or gas emission rates from the ground.

This variation in the degree of confidence of the model to answer different questions means that the expectations of the model must be clearly defined at the outset of the investigation. The intended use of the conceptual model will dictate the questions it needs to address and these in turn will define the investigation techniques that are employed for the acquisition of data.

The following sections describe the specification of investigative work and the application of the conceptual ground gas model.

8.4   DEFINITION AND EXECUTION OF INVESTIGATIVE WORK

The definition and execution of investigative work to characterise a ground gas regime, involves the specification of:

- the type of data or information required

- the source or means of obtaining the data or information

- the quantity of data needed.

The selection of investigative techniques for the measurement of various parameters relevant to the definition of the gas regime requires an understanding of available techniques, their strengths and weaknesses and the type of information they are capable of producing. Figure 8.4 summarises the appropriate techniques to employ to provide information on the various aspects of the gas regime. Reference is made in Figure 8.4 to the Sections of this report which describe the techniques in detail.

The definition of the quantity of data needed for particular statistical confidence levels is a difficult area in relation to gas since it is a mobile contaminant and therefore variable in both time and space. Available guidance is reviewed in Section 7.

8.5   USE OF THE CONCEPTUAL MODEL

The conceptual model of the ground gas regime has two primary functions which may be used for different purposes. These are:

1. The indication of quantities of gas, currently present or likely to occur in the future, at locations in the ground in the vicinity of the gas source.

2. The indication of current or future gas concentrations arising in the ground, or at the ground surface as a result of the gas flows from the source to any specific location.

These fundamental results can be used to satisfy each of the needs of the gas investigation outlined in Section 2 of this report. These specifically relate to the hazards of toxicity, explosivity or asphyxiation, as well as retardation of plant growth or effects on global warming.

In many cases, the use of such a model will be to define the risk of gas hazard at any location or the quantities of gas that control measures will be required to manage.

In this respect, the conceptual model should form the starting point for practitioners involved in ground gas assessments who should follow the development of their model with a risk assessment (see O'Riordan and Milloy, 1993) or the design of protection measures for a proposed development (see Card 1993).

9   Limitations in current practice and recommendations for improvement

This report has considered the practicalities of defining a ground gas by developing a conceptual model based on information and measurements related to the production and movement of gases from the ground. Practical steps can involve defining the source of gas, identifying appropriate field or laboratory methods for measuring gas in the ground and determining the pathways of gas migration. The need to assess factors which influence the behaviour of gas in the ground has also been considered. Throughout the study it has become evident that there is considerable inconsistency amongst practitioners of gas investigations over methods of gas investigation and the interpretation and use of the results. This Section summarises those areas where technical limitations are evident and makes recommendations for possible future improvement.

9.1   LIMITATIONS IN CURRENT PRACTICE

Emphasis on concentrations

The investigation and interpretation of gas-affected ground is currently dominated by the guidance concentrations for methane and carbon dioxide and monitoring presented in WMP 27 and although other documents also give guidance on planning or protection from ground gases (see Section 2), these frequently refer back to WMP 27. WMP 27 has derived the 'trigger' values for ground gases from the occupational exposure limits or explosive levels for the gases concerned. This approach presumes that a gas concentration encountered in the ground could occur in a structure above the ground surface. While this is theoretically possible, it would require a considerable flow of gas from the ground into a poorly ventilated space.

This heavy dependence on 'trigger' concentrations has detracted from the measurement of gas production or surface emission rates which are fundamental factors in the assessment of risk. It is welcome that WMP 26A uses gas flow rates from boreholes as a 'trigger' value for landfill completion, but greater detail of the procedure for making the readings should have been appended.

Interviews undertaken for this study have revealed much uncertainty amongst investigators in the areas of measurement and interpretation of gas concentrations, particularly in connection with only slightly gassing sites. Experienced investigators of gassing sites frequently doubt whether there is in fact a risk on many of the sites despite gas concentrations exceeding the WMP 27 guidance concentrations. This has resulted in some of the regulators developing their own guidance or 'rule of thumb' trigger concentrations. Some ignore CO_2 unless, for example, cellars are to be built. Others make judgements on the basis of how gas concentrations rise after a standpipe has been left open for a few days then resealed.

Design of monitoring installations

The research has revealed widely varying practice amongst investigators on design and installation of gas monitors. Inevitably this leads to an inability to relate results between different investigations. Standardisation of design of gas monitoring installations is essential if they are to be used for flow measurements or other measurements likely to be influenced by the installation design and use. Different approaches are also employed to determine the most appropriate locations for the installations and a suitable frequency of monitoring visits to determine the spatial and temporal variations in the gas regime. While this is often influenced by site conditions, general guidance, particularly for investigations preceding development would be beneficial.

Source identification

Analytical techniques for source identification such as isotope testing are still in their infancy. Although the cost of the testing is reducing, there are insufficient data from different sites to make discrimination between different sources reliable. Similarly there is only limited knowledge on trace gas composition which would assist in the determination of various gas sources.

Definition of migration routes

It is commonly accepted that gas migration is primarily affected by geological conditions, man-made discontinuities and external influences (predominantly climatic). Nevertheless, there is little quantitative information on the manner in which gas moves in the ground and how it can be predicted from observations of gas pressure and concentration.

Use of mathematical models

Some investigators rely heavily upon mathematical modelling both for determining gas production and movement through the ground. These are useful techniques and can provide predictions for future gas production and off-site gas movement under varying climatic conditions. The biggest drawback of these techniques however is the limited validation which has been applied to their performance. The models may have been demonstrated favourably on selected sites but there is insufficient experience and validation to rely on them as the sole means of determining gas emission or production rates.

9.2   RECOMMENDATIONS FOR IMPROVEMENT

The limitations discussed above fall into three broad categories which are:

1.   Insufficient standardisation of sampling and measurement techniques.
2.   Insufficient collated information on ground gas behaviour.
3.   Inadequate guidance on trigger concentrations.

The recommendations necessary to address these limitations and thereby improve the quality of gas investigations and their interpretation are:

Standardisation of investigation techniques

The principal point of confusion in common practice is the lack of standardisation of monitoring installations or standpipes and their use. There would be a major advantage in the provision of standards which cover gas monitoring installations and measurement. Broadly, this could follow the features listed in Table 6.1. The specification presented in a recent guide to site investigations (Thomas Telford, 1993) could provide a useful basis for a standard. However, there should be more stringent control of particular features such as standpipe slot/perforation type. The specification could also cover statistical methods for determining installation locations and frequency of monitoring visits.

There is also a need for the establishment of a more rational testing procedure which is based on the volumes of gas emanating from a piece of ground as well as its composition. While such tests are available, procedures are variable and the interpretation of results is variable.

Collation of current data

There is an increasing quantity of data held by various organisations and statutory authorities which, if combined and collated, could provide invaluable evidence to refine and improve interpretational methods. A national database of records held by statutory authorities such as waste regulation authorities and local authorities could be created. It would prove more difficult (and possibly politically sensitive) to obtain similar information from private organisations such as land owners and waste disposal contractors. The collated data could be used to improve the following:

1. Understanding of factors influencing ground gas.

2. Behaviour of ground gas sources.

3. Zones of influence of monitoring pipes and pumping wells.

4. Validation of mathematical models.

5. Determination of migration pathways.

6. Effectiveness of remedial measures.

7. Occurrence of hazardous incidents resulting from ground gas emissions.

Improvement of current guidance

The current emphasis on concentrations for trigger values is directing attention away from the potentially more important measurement of gas pressures, flows and emission rates. These matters should be given full consideration in future revisions of guidance in common use, in particular WMP 27 and Approved Document C. Urgent attention should therefore be given to revising the guidance in common use, principally Waste Management Paper 27 and Approved Document C to the Building Regulations.

References

AFRC INSTITUTE OF FOOD RESEARCH (1988)
A basic study of landfill microbiology and biochemistry
ETSU B1159
Department of Energy, Harwell Laboratory, Oxfordshire

ARCHER, D.B. and PECK, M.W. (1989)
The microbiology of methane production in landfills.
In: *Microbiology of extreme environments and its potential for biotechnology*. Eds.
Duarte, J.C. and Williams, R.A.D.
Elsevier Applied Science Publishers, London

BRITISH STANDARDS INSTITUTION (BSI)
BS5930: 1981, *Code of practice for site investigations*
DD 175: 1988 Draft for development. *Code of practice for the identification of potentially contaminated land and its investigation.*
BSI, London.

BUSWELL, A.M. and HATFIELD, W.D. (1939)
Anaerobic fermentation
Illinois State Water Survey Bulletin 32, 1-193.

BUSWELL, A.M. and MUELLER, H.F. (1952)
Mechanism of methane fermentation
Industrial and Engineering Chemistry, **44**, 3, 550-552. March 1952.

BUILDING RESEARCH ESTABLISHMENT (1991)
Construction of new buildings on gas contaminated land
Report BR 212 BRE, Garston

CAMPBELL, D.J.V. and CROFT, B.C. (1990)
Landfill gas enhancement: Brogborough test cell programme
In: *Proceedings of International Conference Landfill gas – Energy and Environment '90*, October 1990. Eds. Richards, G.E. and Alston, Y.R.
Harwell Laboratories, Oxfordshire.

CARD, G.B. (1995)
Protecting development from methane
Report 149, CIRIA, London

Clean Air Act (1956)
HMSO, London

COMMISSION OF THE EUROPEAN COMMUNITIES (1993)
Green paper on remedying environmental damage
Communication from the commission to the council and parliament and the economic
and social committee, COM (93) 47 final, May 1993, Cat no. CB-CO-93-147-EN-C.
CEC, Brussels,

CONESTOGA-ROVER AND ASSOCIATES (1981)
Gas recovery and utilisation from a municipal waste disposal site.
Environmental Protection Service Report No. EPS-4-EC-81-2.
Environmental Protection Service, Ottawa, Ontario, Canada.

COOPER, G., GREGORY, R., MANLEY, B.J.W. and NAYLOR, E. (1993a)
*Guidelines for the safe control and utilisation of landfill gas, Part 3 Environmental
Impacts and Law*
ETSU B 1296-P3 DoE Report CWM067C/92
DTI, DoE, OFGAS. Harwell Laboratory, Oxfordshire

COOPER, G., GREGORY, R., MANLEY, B.J.W. and NAYLOR, E. (1993b)
Guidelines for the safe control and utilisation of landfill gas, Part 5 Gas wells.
ETSU B 1296-P5, DoE Report CWM067E/92
DTI, DoE, OFGAS. Harwell Laboratory, Oxfordshire.

COUTTS, D.A.P., DUNK, M. and PUGH, S.Y.R. (1989)
The microbiology of landfills – The Brogborough landfill test cells
In: *UK Department of Energy, Landfill microbiology: R&D Workshop.* Eds Lawson, P.
and Alston, Y.R.
Harwell Laboratories, Oxfordshire.

CREEDY, D.P. (1986)
Methods for the evaluation of seam gas content from measurements on coal samples
Mining Science and Technology, **3**, 141-160.

CREEDY, D.P. (1991)
Methane in coal mines – threats and opportunities
Methane –Facing the problems, 2nd Symposium, Nottingham University, March 1991.

CROWHURST, D. and MANCHESTER, S.J. (1993)
The measurement of methane and associated gases from the ground
Report 131, CIRIA, London.

DoE (1986)
Waste Management Paper No. 26. *Landfilling Wastes*
Department of the Environment, Land Waste Division.
HMSO, London

DoE (1987)
DoE Planning Circular 21/87 (Circular 22/87 : Welsh Office)
Development of contaminated land
HMSO, London

DoE (1988)
DoE Circular 22/88(Circular 44/88 : Welsh Office)
General Development Order Consolidation
HMSO, London

DoE/W.S. ATKINS AND PARTNERS (1988)
Research on landfill gas monitoring equipment and investigation techniques.
Report No. F3350/1988/Dec/1 Volume 2, Investigation techniques

DoE (1989a)
Waste Management Paper No 27. *The control of landfill gas*
Department of the Environment, Wastes Technical Division
HMSO, London.

DoE (1989b)
Planning Circular 17/89 (Circular 38/89 : Welsh Office)
Landfill sites : development control
HMSO, London

DoE/HOWARD HUMPHREYS AND PARTNERS LTD. (1990)
Report on comparison of methods of assessing landfill gas potential.
Report 83.404.0, DoE Waste Technical Division research programme.
DoE, London.

DoE (1991)
Waste Management Paper No 27 *Landfill gas (2nd Edition)*
Department of the Environment, Wastes Technical Division
HMSO, London

DoE (1992)
The Building Regulations Approved Document C
HMSO, London

DoE (1993)
Waste Management Paper No 26A *Landfill Completion*
Department of the Environment, Wastes Technical Division
HMSO, London

DoE/Wardell Armstrong (1993)
Progress report on DoE Research contract PECD 7/1/445 *Methane and other gases from disused coal mines*
September 1993

DoE (1994)
Waste Management Paper No. 4 *Licensing of Waste Management Facilities (3rd Edition)*
Department of the Environment, Wastes Technical Division
HMSO, London

DOLFING, J. and MULDER, J-W. (1985)
Comparison of methane production rate and coenzyme F_{420} content of methanogenic consortia in anaerobic granular sludge.
Applied and Environmental Microbiology. Volume 49, 5, pp 1142-1145.
American Society for Microbiology

ELLIOT, L.F. and McCALLA, T.M. (1972)
The composition of the soil atmosphere beneath a beef cattle feedlot and a cropped field
Proceedings of the Soil Science Society of America. Volume 36, pp 68-70.

EMBERTON, J.R. (1986)
The biological and chemical characterisation of landfills.
In: *Energy from landfill gas.* Proceedings of a conference jointly sponsored by the UK Department of Energy and the US Department of Energy, Solihull, UK. October 1986.
Eds Emberton, J.R. and Emberton, R.F.

EMCON ASSOCIATES (1981)
State of the art of methane gas enhancement in landfills
Argonne National Laboratory, MSW-LG, USA.

Environmental Protection Act (1990)
HMSO, London

FARQUHAR, G.F and ROVERS, F.A. (1973)
Gas production during refuse decomposition.
Water, Air and Soil Pollution. 2, 483 – 495

FERGUSON, C.C. (1992)
The statistical basis for spatial sampling of contaminated land.
Ground Engineering, Vol. 25, No. 5 June 1992, 34-8

GHABAEE, K. and RODWELL, W.R. (1989)
Landfill gas modelling, a literature survey of landfill gas generation and migration
Atomic Energy Authority Report No. R2567, Petroleum Reservoir Technology
Division, AEA Winfrith.

HARRIES, C.R. (1989)
Landfill Microbiology – Work supported at Biotal by the Department of the
Environment
In: *UK Department of Energy, Landfill Microbiology:R&D Workshop*, Eds. Lawson, P.
and Alston, Y.R.
Harwell Laboratory, UK AEA.

HARRIES, C.R. (1991)
The application of laboratory methods to the evaluation of methane production.
In: *Methane – Facing the problems syposium*. Nottingham,UK, March 1991.

HITCHMAN, S.P., DARLING, W.G. and WILLIAMS, G.M. (1990)
Stable isotope ratios in methane containing gases in the United Kingdom
British Geological Survey, Keyworth. Technical Report WE/89/30

HMIP (1988)
Waste Management Paper No 4(1976) 2nd Edition.
The licensing of waste facilities
Her Majesty's Inspectorate of Pollution
HMSO, London

HOEKS, J. (1983)
Significance of biogas production in waste tips.
Waste Management and Research **1**, 323-325.

HOVLAND, M and JUDD, A.G. (1992)
The global production of methane from shallow submarine sources
In: Methane in Marine Sediments, Ed: Davis, A.M.
Continental Shelf Research **12**, 10, 1992.
Pergamon Press

HSE (1985)
The Abbeystead disaster
HMSO, London

HUDSON, J.A. (1989)
Rock mechanics principles in engineering practice
CIRIA B6, CIRIA/Butterworth Heinemann.

HUDSON, J.A. (1992)
Rock engineering systems
Ellis Horwood

INSTITUTE OF PETROLEUM (1993)
Code of practice for the investigation and mitigation of possible petroleum-based land cotamination
The Institute of Petroleum, London, February 1993.

INSTITUTION OF CIVIL ENGINEERS (1989)
Specification for ground investigation
Thomas Telford, London

INTERDEPARTMENTAL COMMITTEE ON THE REDEVELOPMENT OF
CONTAMINATED LAND (1987)
Guidance Note 59/83.*Guidance on the assessment and redevelopment of contaminated land*
(2nd Edition)
DoE

INTERDEPARTMENTAL COMMITTEE ON THE REDEVELOPMENT OF
CONTAMINATED LAND (1990)
Guidance Note 17/78.*Notes on the development and after use of landfill sites*
(8th Edition)
DoE

KNOX, K. (1990)
The relationship between leachate and gas
In: *Proceedings of International Conference, Landfill gas – Energy and Environment '90*, October 1990. Eds. Richards, G.E. and Alston, Y.R.
Harwell Laboratories, Oxfordshire.

LEWIN, K. and BRADSHAW, K. (1993)
Continuous monitoring of methane in groundwater
HSE Contract research report No.49/1993
HMSO, London

LYTWYNSHYN, G.R., ZIMMERMAN, R.E., FLYNN, N.W., WINGENDER, R. and
OLIVERI, V. (1982)
Landfill methane recovery : part II – Gas Characterisation
Argonne National Laboratory, ANL/CNSV-TM-118. IL(USA)

LOHANI, B.N. and KO, S.M. (1988)
Optimal sampling of domestic solid waste
Journal of Environmental Engineering, Vol. 114, No.6, 1479-1483.

LOUSLEY, J.E. (1976)
Wild flowers of chalk and limestone
Collins New Naturalist Series, Bloomsbury Books, London Reprinted 1976

METHODS FOR THE EXAMINATION OF WATERS AND ASSOCIATED
MATERIALS (1988)
The determination of methane and other hydrocarbon gases in water.
HMSO, London.

NCB (1979)
Ventilation in coal mines – a handbook for colliery ventilation officers
National Coal Board.

O'GILBERT, R. (1987)
Statistical methods for environmental pollution monitoring
Van Nostrand Reinhold, New York

O'RIORDAN, N.J. and MILLOY, C. (1995)
Risk assessment for methane and other gases from the ground
Report 152, CIRIA, London

PACEY, J. and AUGENSTEIN, D. (1990)
Modelling landfill methane generation
In: *Proceedings of International Conference, Landfill gas – Energy and Environment
'90*, October 1990. Eds. Richards, G.E. and Alston, Y.R.
Harwell Laboratories, Oxfordshire.

PARTRIDGE, R.H. and CURTIS, I.H. (1986)
*Final report on the methane measurements made with the NPL diode laser remote
monitoring system at New Park landfill site, Ugley, Stansted, Essex*
National Physical Laboratory Report, Qu S26.

PECK, M.W. and ARCHER, D.B. (1989)
Methods for the quantification of methanogenic bacteria
International Industrial Biotechnology. Volume 9, 3.

PECKSEN, G.N. (1985)
Methane and the development of derelict land
London Environmental Supplement No. 13, Summer 1985

POHLAND, F.G. (1986)
Critical review and summary of leachate and gas production from landfills.
United States Environmental Protection Agency report 600/2-86/073.
Georgia Institute of Technology, Atlanta, Ga. USA.

REES, J.F. (1980)
Optimisation of methane production and refuse decomposition in landfills by
temperature control.
Journal of Chemical Technology and Biotechnology **30,** 458-465

RAYBOULD, J.G., ROWAN, S. and BARRY, D. (1995)
Methane investigation strategies
Report 150, CIRIA, London

SLEAT, R., HARRIES, C., VINEY, I. and REES, J.F. (1989)
Activities and distribution of key microbial groups in landfill
In: *Sanitary landfilling: Process,Technology and Environmental Impact.* Eds.
Christensen, T.H., Cossu, R. and Stegmann, R. pp 51-59.
Academic Press, London.

STAFF, M.G., SIZER, K.E. and NEWSON, S.R. (1991)
The potential for surface emissions of methane from abandoned mine workings
In: *Methane –Facing the problems syposium.* Nottingham, UK, March 1991.

SVENSSON, B.H. (1976)
Methane production in tundra peat
In: *Microbial production and utilisation of gases (H_2, CH_4, CO_2).* Eds. Schlegl, H.G.,
Gottschalk, G. and Phennig, N. 135-139.
E. Goltze kg Gottingen.

THOMAS TELFORD (1993)
Site investigation series – 4, Part 3 – Specification for ground investigation
Thomas Telford, London.

UEHLING, M. (1993)
Keeping rubbish rotten to the core
New Scientist 1888, 28 August 1993, pp 12-13.

WALTON, A.N. and HARDMAN, C.E. (1973)
*Climatological memorandum No.51A, Averages of sea level barometric pressures at 9h
for the United Kingdom 1941 – 1970.*
Meteorological Office, Climatological services UDC 551.542(41/42), 551.543.6

WARREN SPRING LABORATORY (1990)
United Kingdom acid rain monitoring
Air pollution division, Warren Spring Laboratory, Stevenage, Herts. UK.

THE WATT COMMITTEE ON ENERGY (1993)
Methane emissions. Papers presented at the 29th conference of the Watt Committee on Energy, held on 28 January 1993 at the Royal Geographical Society, London. Ed. Professor A. Williams
The Watt Committee on Energy.

WIDDICK, D.A. and EMBLEY, T.M. (1992)
Use of nucleic acid technology in landfill – a feasibility study
Energy Technology Support Unit Report B 1315
Department of Trade and Industry.

WILLIAMS, G.M. and AITKENHEAD, N. (1989)
The gas explosion at Loscoe, Derbyshire
Methane – Facing the problems symposium, Paper 3.6 , Nottingham, 26-28 September 1989.

WYMAN, V. (1994)
Landfill gases under cover
Surveyor 19 May 1994. **181,** 5292, 12-15

YAVITT, J.V. and LANG, G. E. (1988)
Potential methane production and methane oxidation rates in peatland ecosystems of the Appalachian mountains, United States.
Global Biogeochemical Cycles **2,** 3, 253-268.

YOUNG, A. (1990)
Volumetric changes in landfill gas flux in response to variations in atmospheric pressure
Waste Management and Research (1990), 8, 379-385

YOUNG, A., LATHAM, B. and GRAHAM, G. (1993)
Atmospheric pressure effects on gas migration.
Wastes Management, April 1993.

YOUNG, P. J. (1989)
Landfill gas –The role of the consultant, 'Expertise or Explosions'
Paper presented at the Institution of Environmental Health Officers meeting on landfill gas, King's College, London. 11 April 1989.

CIRIA Report 151   1995

Books are to be returned on or
the last date below.

2 6 MAY 1998 ◇

...urements of gas

...ton and J M McEntee

D
624
HAR

CIRIA

CONSTRUCTION INDUSTRY RESEARCH AND INFORMATION ASSOCIATION
6 Storey's Gate, Westminster, London SW1P 3AU
E-mail switchboard @ ciria.org.uk
Tel 0171-222 8891   Fax 0171-222 1708

Summary

Rational judgements about the risks to development from ground gases, such as methane, carbon dioxide and landfill gas, rely upon understanding the gas/water/ground regime. Gas measurements, taken during an investigation of a site, provide part of the evidence from which to postulate a reliable model of the gas source and its pathways of movement. But valid interpretation depends upon valid measurements. This report provides guidance for engineers to test the validity of gas measurements and their meaning. Its purpose is to assist those planning, undertaking and interpreting gas investigations to take sensible measurements and to make sense of the measurements taken. The report shows how the systems of measurement affect the values measured, how external conditions alter the gas regime, and how, by recognising what has and has not been measured, the results of the measurements can be interpreted in the site context. For example, measurements of composition (often as concentrations of one gas in a mixture) are not sufficient on their own. They are indications of presence, but not of quantities of gas being produced or of the potential to produce it. The report reviews the limitations of current gas measurement techniques and recommends ways to standardise and improve not only the techniques of measurement but also the ways to develop sound interpretations.

HARRIES, C R, WITHERINGTON, P J and McENTEE, J M
Interpreting measurements of gas in the ground
Construction Industry Research and Information Association
Report 151, 1995

© CIRIA 1995

Keywords:		
Methane, Carbon dioxide, Landfill gas, Field measurement, Reliability, Interpretation		
Reader Interest:	**Classification**	
Construction, geotechnical and environmental engineers and scientists, local authorities, waste management.	AVAILABILITY CONTENT STATUS USER	Restricted Guidance document Committee guided Environmental and geotechnical engineers

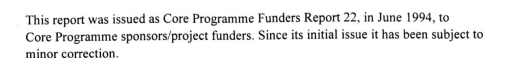

This report was issued as Core Programme Funders Report 22, in June 1994, to Core Programme sponsors/project funders. Since its initial issue it has been subject to minor correction.